A Bridge Between Two Worlds

The fish he swims in the sea
Man he walks on the land
In separate worlds they'll forever be
Who thinks a fish wants to stand?

The fish, he breathes the water
Man, he breathes the air
But my friend had a daughter
A mermaid with golden hair

Her father was a man
Her mother was a fish
She lived in both worlds
What more could you wish?

By day she swam in the sea
At night she sang to the moon
In worlds that would never meet
One soul played a happy tune

And the sailors that heard her sing
Wished they had fins and gills
On that same rock they would cling
Her voice gave lonely men thrills

So, whenever you find youself sneering
At the creatures that live in the drink
Don't be so sure what you're comparing
They're not as different as you think!

W. Williams

Introduction

Fishes are the most numerous vertebrates on earth, numbering more than 23,000 living species. Many scientists speculate that fishes have been around for as long as 500 million years, predating birds, mammals, reptiles, amphibians, and even flowering plants. Other scientists suggest fishes, as well as all other plants and animals, are much younger than that great age.

Fishes have adapted well to the great changes that have occurred throughout the earth's history. As a group, fishes have stood the test of time. They also have spread around the world in a variety of habitats. The variety in appearance and behavior among fishes staggers the mind. Some fishes are adapted to saltwater environments, others to fresh water, and still others move freely between the two realms. They range in size from less than 1/4 inch to possibly 60 feet. Some fish resemble legendary sea monsters while some pretend to be rocks. Some fish live alone, while others live in schools of thousands. Some fish fly, and some fish walk. Some fish angle for dinner, and some farm other fish. Many fish are brightly hued, but most fish aren't. Some fish glow in the dark. Many fish travel thousands of miles in their lifetimes, while other fish remain loyal to a home territory the size of a baseball.

This great body of organisms called "fishes" displays a breadth of life as grand as the earth itself. Florida, more than many other parts of the earth, shares abundantly in this wealth of fishes.

CLASSIFYING FISHES

Ichthyologists (scientists who study fishes) arrange fishes in groups related by certain internal and external features.

There are four taxonomic classes of living fish: Myxini (hagfishes), Cephalaspidomorphi (lampreys), Chondrichthyes (cartilaginous fishes, including sharks and rays), and Actinopterygii (bony fishes). These classes are further organized into orders, families, genera, and species.

Physical features provide important aids in classifying fishes. Fin rays, for instance, are often used in classifying fishes. The rays are spines that protrude from a fish's body and are typically webbed to form the various fins, including the caudal (tail), dorsal (back), anal, pelvic (ventral), and pectoral fins. In soft-rayed fishes, the spines of the fins are generally flexible, as their name implies, and are composed of two rays that are mirror images of one another.

Another physical characteristic used to classify fishes is the location of the pelvic fins. Most people with some knowledge of anatomy would probably expect pelvic fins to be located on the abdomen. In many fishes they are, but in other fishes, the pelvic fins are situated farther forward.

Different scientists consider certain features to be more or less important as classification tools. Consequently, there is much disagreement over the "correct" classification of a species.

FRESH WATER VS SALT WATER IN FLORIDA FISHES

Around 1,000 species of saltwater fishes live in Florida's marine habitats (full strength sea water above 200 meters depth) for at least a portion of their lives. Some are year-round residents. Others are seasonal visitors. A few are rare strays from other parts of the world. About 230 species of freshwater fishes live in Florida, including species which are ordinarily marine fishes but which regularly enter freshwater environments. Distinguishing between freshwater and saltwater fishes can get complicated because of the difficulty, at times, in setting precise limits on the two types of habitats.

Most states find no problem defining a freshwater fish. Those states have no coastline. Several states have a coastal connection and may be the temporary homes for a few anadromous species such as striped bass, or catadromous fishes, such as American eels. Anadromous fishes spend most of their lives in the ocean but migrate upstream in freshwater rivers to spawn. Catadromous fishes do just the opposite, spending most of their lives in freshwater environments but migrating to the sea to spawn. Even so, the number of species is small, and their migrations are defined rather well.

Florida, on the other hand, is a large peninsula. Yet Florida contains extensive freshwater systems, too. A large number of marine fishes find relatively easy access to Florida's extensive Atlantic and Gulf coasts. Many of these species occur naturally in brackish water of less than five ppt (parts per thousand) salinity, and several freshwater species tolerate similar brackish conditions. For instance, the marine pinfish is one of the two dominant species of larger fishes in the springs around Crystal River on Florida's Gulf Coast.

The water bodies, themselves, can be hard to classify. Tide and rainfall influence how far upstream salt water penetrates and when. Florida is relatively low and flat, and salt water can extend far upstream. At some point in these rivers, a fresh/brackish water transition zone will exist with the tongue of salty water lying beneath the tongue of fresh water, because salt water is denser. Periods with little or no rain permit tidal action to push salty water farther upstream. Periods of heavy rain push the salty water back out. In some locations, salt springs create localized zones of salinity farther upstream than tidal flow would ordinarily carry salt water.

WHAT IS A FISH?

A fish is an aquatic, cold-blooded vertebrate (animal with a backbone) that possesses both fins and gills throughout its life. It is this combination of characteristics that distinguishes fish from other aquatic animals. Tadpoles, for instance, have gills. but as these larvae mature into frogs, they lose their gills. Marine animals such as squid and octopi possess gills, but like other mullusks, they lack a backbone. Such animals are invertebrates, and as such cannot be fish. Many creatures of the sea such as starfish, crayfish, and jellyfish share the fish name, but, lacking a backbone, are not fish. Marine mammals, such as whales and dolpins, have backbones, but lack gills.

WHAT IS A FLORIDA FISH?

Many fish live out their lives entirely in Florida. Other species just pass through Florida waters on their migratory journeys. Quite a few non-native (exotic) fish were brought to Florida from far-away places and now live quite well in the waters of the Sunshine State. Boundary lines in the ocean are far from precise. In a book like this, the problem of deciding what is a Florida fish must be resolved somehow. It has been arbitrarily decided to cover those species that live at least part of their lives in Florida in waters out to depths of about 600 feet (100 fathoms).

HOW THIS BOOK IS ORGANIZED

***Florida's Fabulous Fishes** is arranged by taxonomic order and family in phylogenetic sequence. More than 500 species of freshwater and marine fish are described. Some species are included for their fascinating life histories, or because their appearance is particularly striking.*

Jawless Fishes

Lampreys
(Family Petromyzontidae)

"Ugly" is in the eye of the beholder, of course, but beholding a lamprey for the first time might bring forth such a pronouncement—maybe even the second or third time. Their eating habits don't improve their image either.

Jawless and eel-like, the lamprey has 20 or so North American species, but only two occur in Florida: the sea lamprey and the southern brook lamprey. The southern brook lamprey is restricted to fresh water, while the parasitic sea lamprey attaches to host fish in both fresh and salt water. All lampreys have cartilaginous skeletons.

The sea lamprey may grow up to four feet in length. It attaches to a host fish by rasping a small hole into the fish's side with its many-toothed oral disk, the closest thing it has to a mouth. Then it sucks out its host's blood and body fluids. As might be expected, frequently the host dies.

A landlocked population of sea lampreys has spawned the largest species eradication program in US history due to its destructive impact on the commercial and sport fishery in the Great Lakes. Fortunately for Florida's fishery, sea lampreys need cold streams to breed.

In contrast, the southern brook lamprey grows only to seven inches in length and is not parasitic. In fact, it doesn't feed at all as an adult.

The larvae of lampreys, called ammocoetes, are blind filter feeders that live up to five years in the silty stream bottoms. Here they consume algae and detritus that get trapped in mucus in the branchial chamber and are then passed into the intestines. The larval stage lasts two to three years, and metamorphosis to adult takes three to six months.

VU

Top: **The oral disk of a large, parasitic lamprey showing the many teeth that allows it to rasp a hole in its prey.**

HOW FISHES BREATHE

Almost all fishes breathe by taking in water through the mouth and forcing it past the gills and out the gill slits. A membrane at the edge of the operculum (gill cover) prevents water from entering back through the gill opening. Most fishes possess four pairs of gill arches, each with two rows of gill filaments. The red, finger-like filaments are rich with blood and form a "curtain" between the mouth cavity and the gill cavity. The gill filaments extract up to 95% of the oxygen dissolved in the water as the water passes through this curtain. Fishes need such respiratory efficiency because water is so dense it holds only about 1/30 of the oxygen normally held in the air.

THE TROUBLE WITH EXOTICS

Recognizing native species is becoming more important as non-native, or exotic fishes spread across the Florida. Many of these species originated with releases from aquariums or fish farms. Others were introduced by the state government, for aquatic weed control or as a sport fish. In Johann Wyss' famous classic, ***The Swiss Family Robinson****, the Robinson family introduced rabbits onto Whale Island. Without natural enemies, the rabbits multiplied rapidly, creating a plentiful supply of meat and skins for the Robinsons. It makes a good story. Yet Wyss only hints at the trouble brewing from this non-native introduction. "The young and tender shoots of the trees bore the marks of many greedy, mischievous little teeth."*

Unless the rabbits were harvested sufficiently, they would eventually overpopulate the island, starving themselves and reducing the island's carrying capacity below its original level. In the meantime, the rabbits probably would have outcompeted any native plant-eaters on the island.

Such mischief isn't always fiction. Exotic species really can disrupt an established ecosystem and displace native species. It's nearly impossible to foretell accurately all the consequences of non-native introductions. Florida experiences extreme problems con-cerning exotic plants and animals due in part to Florida's temperate, sub-tropical, and tropical climates, but also due to the great number of exotics brought into the state and grown here. Walking catfish from Asia, tilapia from Africa, and oscars from South America find Florida quite to their liking.

DP/Seapics.com

INTRODUCTION TO THE CLASS CHONDRICHTHYES

Like lampreys, the skeletons of Chondrichthyes are made of cartilage. That is where the similarity ends. All Chondrichthyes have well-developed jaws, paired nostrils, and paired pelvic and pectoral fins. In other words, they look more like fish. They also lack a swim bladder and sink if they stop swimming. Fertilization in sharks, skates, and rays takes place internally. Many species give birth to live young, while others encase eggs in leathery or horn-like sacs and deposit them on the sea floor. In males, a portion of the pelvic fins is modified into a copulatory organ, called a clasper.

The Chondrichthyes benefit from a specialized sensory system not found in other fishes. A special group of cells around the head, called the ampullae of Lorenzini, enable sharks, skates, and rays to sense the minute electric field transmitted from other fishes, in fact, from all living animals. Sharks, in particular, use their electrosensory system to capture prey. During the last few seconds of capture, when a shark may lose sight of its victim, the shark's sensory system enables it to orient its jaws toward its prey.

SQUALENE - A SHARK PRODUCT

Squalene is a substance found in the human body as well as in the liver of sharks. Called a precursor, it helps the body form other necessary substances such as cholesterol. Squalene obtained from sharks is sold worldwide in the form of capsules, creams, or oils. It is promoted as a beauty and health product for which many claims are made, from boosting the immune system to improving the skin. It is known that squalene is a moisterizer that also helps heal burns, but beyond that, there is little scientific evidence to support the many other claims. Yet, heavy promotion of squalene products has had an impact on shark populations.

Carpet Sharks and Their Allies

Nurse Sharks

(Family Ginglymostomatidae)

The nurse shark's name might have come from a noise it makes when feeding, which some people think sounds like a baby nursing.

The nurse shark is the only member of the order Orectolobiform in Florida. This common reef fish is typically seen resting on the sea floor and is easily distinguished from other sharks by: barbels at the front of each nostril and two nearly equal-sized dorsal fins. Nurse sharks are normally rather sluggish and eat small fish, crustaceans, and sea urchins. Nurse sharks are born alive after hatching from eggs within the mother's uterus.

***Top:* A young nurse shark. This species is often seen by divers, but is not especially dangerous because of the small size of its teeth.**

R&VT/Seapics.com

Whale Shark

(Family Rhincodontidae)

Rare in Florida waters, the whale shark is the world's largest living fish, reaching over 45 feet in length and weighing more than 26,000 pounds. Despite its huge size, the whale shark is a slow-moving, harmless filter feeder. The shark's gill rakers strain plankton and small fishes washing from the water into its mouth and out its gills.

Whale sharks have often been observed feeding in a peculiar vertical position, with heads pointed toward the surface. Whale sharks usually stay near the surface in the open ocean and occasionally are struck by vessels.

Females are live-bearers and can produce hundreds of baby sharks, each up to two feet long.

Top: **the scale of the diver in this photo shows that this is truly the largest fish in the world.**

Bottom: **another view of the whale shark showing its whitish spots and the three ridges on its back.**

MN/Seapics.com

Ground Sharks

(Order Carchariniformes)

This order contains the most species of living sharks, with eight families and more than 200 species.

Cat Sharks

(Family Scyliorhinidae)

With more than 100 species, the Scyliorhinidae is the largest shark family. Cat sharks are small, bottom-dwelling sharks, named for their distinctive cat-like eyes. The chain dogfish is usually found living in offshore waters deeper than 500 feet. This boldly-marked but rarely-seen fish encloses its eggs in a tough case with tendrils at each corner that wrap around debris on the ocean floor. Little is known of this fish's feeding habits. However, investigators have found small stones in the stomachs of these sharks, suggesting they feed on the bottom.

DP/Seapics.com

Top: **a chain dogfish, one of the hundred or more species of cat sharks worldwide.**

Hound Sharks

(Family Triakidae)

Hound sharks usually grow to less than four feet long. The family includes 35 species and is represented in all warm and temperate coastal seas. The smooth dogfish is one of possibly three species of hound sharks found in Florida. It is a relatively small but common, bottom-dwelling shark living in near-shore waters out to about 1,200 feet deep. Hardly a terror, this shark possesses molar-like teeth it uses to crush crustaceans and small fishes. Smooth dogfish are live-bearing, with litters of up to 20 young. The smaller Florida smooth-hound may be even more poorly known than the smooth dogfish.

CANCER IN SHARKS

In a nutshell, it hardly ever happens. In fact, the incidence of tumor formation in sharks is so rare that scientists are studying them in the hope of one day finding better drug therapies for cancer. It seems the sharks' primitive immune system is more effective in certain ways than the highly specialized immune system of mammals.

In mammals, immune cells originate in the bone marrow and other sites. Once mature, these cells enter the blood stream where they can fight invading substances, such as carcinogens. However, a time lag occurs before immune cells become available to attack the offending substance. Sharks lack bone—thus, no bone marrow. Immune cells of sharks originate in the spleen, thymus, and certain other tissues. Some maturation occurs in these tissues, but many immune cells mature in the shark's bloodstream. Studies at the Mote Marine Laboratory in Sarasota suggest immune cells already in a shark's bloodstream may attack foreign substances with no time lag.

Apparently, there is another advantage to being primitive. Whereas mammals produce several classes of immunoglobulins (antibodies), sharks produce only one, termed IgM. What shark antibodies lack in variety, they make up for in sheer volume. Sharks normally have IgM circulating at very high levels in their blood, apparently ready to overwhelm invaders.

THE TEETH OF SHARKS

A shark's teeth are the only part of the shark's skeleton containing calcium carbonate, a hard mineral which survives long enough to become fossilized. The rest of the shark's skeleton is not made of bone like that of other animals, but is composed of organic cartilage which rots immediately upon the creature's death.

The fossilized teeth of many sea creatures can be found on the beach. But shark's teeth are more numerous because sharks lose teeth and regenerate new ones throughout their lives. A large shark may produce 20,000 teeth during its lifetime. Also, shark's teeth are more obvious because they are much larger and less likely to have been worn down through the years.

Sharks teeth may be found on Florida beachs, but are particularly numerous on the beach at Venice, Florida. A person going to Venice beach to hunt for shark's teeth will not go home empty-handed. Lucky collectors might even find a tooth of the extinct carcharodon megalodon, the 50-100 foot predecessor to the great white shark. Four-inch specimens of its huge teeth are not an unusual find at Venice, and the largest specimens may reach eight inches.

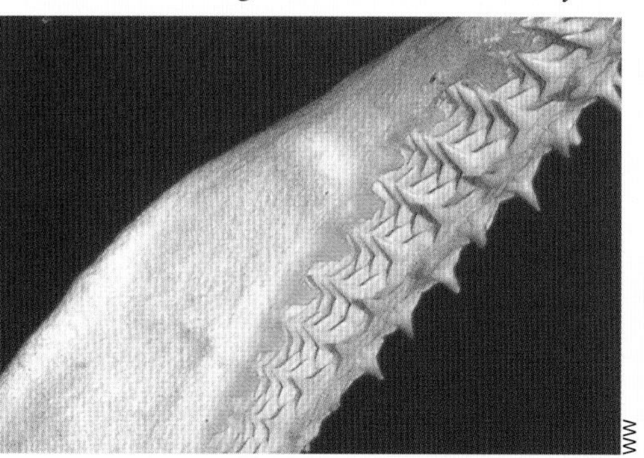

WW

Above: **a view of a shark's jaw showing rows of replacement teeth lined up, waiting to advance forward as old teeth are lost.**

PC AT SEA PLEAURES AND TREASURES

Above: **an assortment of shark's teeth, all of which may be found at the beach at Venice.**

Requiem Sharks

(Family Carcharhinidae)

Requiem sharks, or "whalers," are renowned for their large size, toothy maws, and carnivorous habits. Some often congregate in large "masses" near the surface, and this tendency was noted in a rather far-fetched comparison to the crowd which gathers for a Catholic mass for the dead, or a requiem. These fish have the classic, streamlined, shark-look. Several sharks generally regarded as dangerous, including the bull shark, tiger shark, and oceanic whitetip shark, belong to this family.

As many as 17 species of requiem sharks find their respective territories from the surf line to the immense depths beyond the continental shelf off Florida.

Lemon sharks and reef sharks are common inhabitants of reefs and, along with the nurse shark, may be the sharks most often seen by divers. Lemon sharks can be found in shallow waters such as mangrove bays. The bull shark is the only shark in Florida to enter fresh water. The oceanic whitetip shark is seldom seen because it lives in open ocean, but its presence has been noted dramatically at times. This shark is the one most often implicated in fatalities associated with mid-ocean plane crashes and shipwrecks, most notably the sinking of the American cruiser Indianapolis near the end of World War II.

The tiger shark is one of the most dangerous sharks in tropical waters. It is well-known for its varied menu. Stomach content studies have identified fish, crabs, birds, coal, garbage, other sharks, sea turtles, marine mammals, and the occasional human.

The tiger shark is ovoviviparous, while all other requiem sharks are viviparous.

Top: **the tiger shark is common off Florida's coasts and could be Florida's most dangerous shark because it can reach 18 feet and often swims close to shore. It has attacked waders in shallow water.**

Bottom: **the lemon shark is one of the few sharks whose habitat is in and around reefs.**

MU/Seapics.com

DP/Seapics.com

Top: Caribbean reef shark. The shark has also been called the sleeping shark because it is often seen resting quietly during the day.

Left: bull shark. The bull shark can live in salt water or fresh water and has been found more than 1,000 miles up the Mississippi River! It is considered very dangerous to people.

Bottom, left and right: oceanic whitetip shark. This shark may be involved in attacks on marine disaster victims floating in the ocean. Note the white tip of the dorsal fin.

MU/Seapics.com

MU/Seapics.com

DF/Seapics.com

JW/Seapics.com

All the sharks on this page can be considered dangerous to humans, although the Atlantic sharpnose shark is less dangerous because of its smaller size.

Top: a silky shark, so named because of its smooth skin texture.

Left: blacktip shark.

Bottom, right: Atlantic sharpnose shark.

Bottom, left: sandbar shark.

DF/Seapics.com

DF/Seapics.com

Top: **a blue shark. Note its distinctive long and slender snout.**

SHARKS AND HUMANS

Sharks do attack people, that's a fact. Put that fact in perspective, however. The world contains 350 species of sharks, or thereabouts. Of these, 80% don't exceed five feet and pose little, if any, risk to people. In fact, people rarely encounter many of them. Only 32 species are known to have attacked people; 36 more may be potentially dangerous. Though any shark six feet or longer can pose a risk to humans, only two species have been identified as repeat offenders, so to speak: tiger and bull sharks. The great white shark is a threat, but only rarely enters Florida waters.

Potentially the most dangerous sharks for swimmers in the Gulf are the bull, tiger, lemon, and the larger hammerhead sharks. Nurse sharks are sometimes implicated in bites to divers. However, thrill-seeking divers often approach these sluggish reef dwellers, and the shark's response in such cases can hardly be called unprovoked.

The International Shark Attack File (ISAF) is a record of all known shark attacks on humans around the world and is administered by the American Elasmobranch Society and the Florida Museum of Natural History at the University of Florida. ISAF records suggest that sharks attack 70-100 people each year worldwide, with 5-15 fatalities. That is about six percent of the number of people struck by lightning each year in the US.

Many shark attacks occur in near-shore waters. Unprovoked attacks usually take one of three forms. "Hit-and-run" attacks typically occur in the surf zone with swimmers and surfers. The shark makes a single bite or slash and swims away, often unseen by the victim. Injuries in these attacks are seldom life threatening. Hit-and-run attacks may be a case of mistaken identity, especially in murky, turbulent surf.

"Bump-and-bite" attacks are less common than hit-and-run attacks but cause far greater injury and many more fatalities, mostly to divers and swimmers in deeper water. The shark initially circles and sometimes bumps its victim prior to attacking.

"Sneak" attacks occur without warning. Both sneak attacks and bump-and-bite attacks commonly involve repeat attacks on the victim and cause severe injury and often death.

Despite the gruesome tales of shark attacks, humans most often weigh in on the other side of the ledger. People kill between 20 and 100 million sharks each year. Most of these sharks are taken through commercial and recreational fishing for food and sport. A large market exists around the world for shark meat and fins, and a market is growing for shark products in medicine. Shark corneas are sometimes transplanted into human eyes, and shark cartilage is sometimes used in treating burn victims. Shark-liver oil is used in preparing medications for hemorrhoids and as a source of the anti-oxidant, squalene.

Studies were conducted in the 1980's at MIT and at Mote Marine Laboratory in Sarasota involving both shark and cow cartilage. Researchers attempted to determine how cartilage naturally resists penetration by blood capillaries. At that time, researchers thought new drug therapies might be developed if the mechanism for this inhibition could be indentified. Such a drug might be able to inhibit the spread of blood vessels that feed a concerous tumor or arthritic inflammation.

However, this research showed that unnaturally large concentrations of the active material in cartilage were required to produce any inhibiting effect in test animals. Also, the active material could be extracted and concentated only after several weeks of harsh chemical procedures, and very large amonts of raw cartilage were required.

Following these studies, the researchers concluded that cartilage in any animal "probably plays no active role in disease resistance in the living animal."

Unfortunately, sharks are harvested to produce "medicinal" products with no proven value. Dried shark cartilage pills are being promoted as cures for cancer and arthritis. However, research into the role of cartilage in sharks' uncanny resistance to cancer does not support the claims of these pill pushers—far from it, in fact.

In the end, one fact is clear. As someone once said, "Sharks don't eat many people, but people eat a great many sharks."

THE SEX LIVES OF SHARKS

All Chondrichthyes reproduce by the male placing his sperm into the body of the female (internal fertilization), in a manner similar to that of humans and other mammals. Most (but not all) other fish reproduce by spawning, in which the female, while swimming close to the male, releases her eggs directly into the water at the same time as the male releases his sperm (milt). The eggs are fertilized when they come into contact with the sperm in the water (external fertilization). Although all chondrichthyes utilize internal fertilization, not all reproduce alike. Some, including catsharks and skates, are oviparous (egg-laying). These species produce encapsulated eggs in a tough case with horns, popularly called a "mermaid's purse." Inside this case, each embryo is attached to a yolk sac from which it draws nutrition. When the yolk sac is exhausted, the young hatch and swim away to a life on their own. Viviparous species (live-bearers) employ different reproductive methods. The sand tiger shark and many rays produce eggs that hatch inside the mother. The embryos are not attached to the womb but are nourished by their yolk sac and a secretion known as "uterine milk." Sand tiger embryos consume any eggs their mothers produce. O0nly two pups survive, one in each uterus. In other viviparous sharks, including hammerheads, the yolk sac becomes modified into a placenta and attaches to the wall of the uterus. Nurse sharks, in a sense, combine reproductive methods. These ovoviviparous sharks hatch from eggs contained in the mother's uterus and are then born alive.

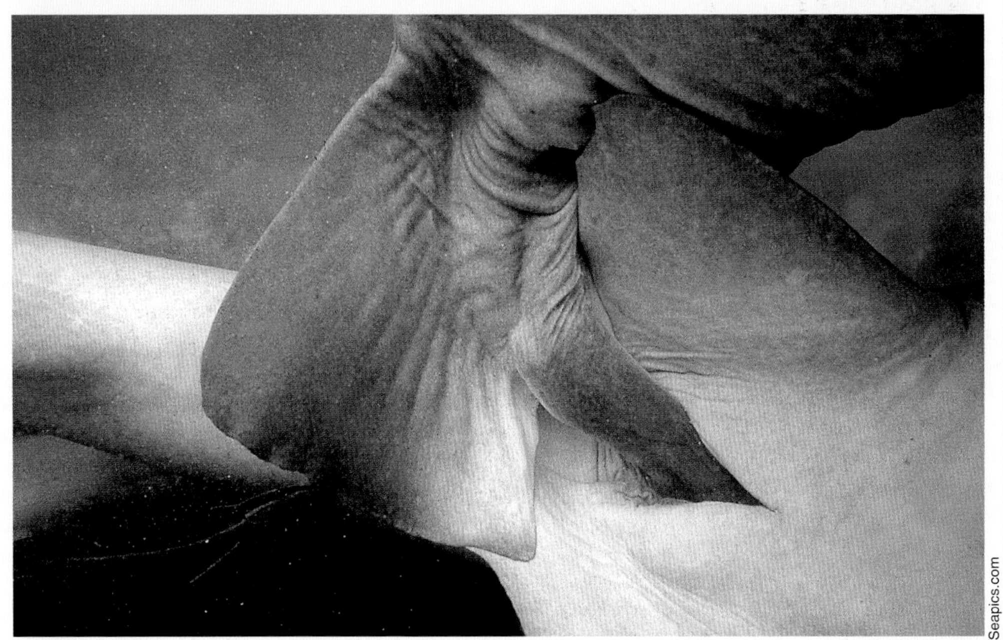

Top, left: **sharks courting. The male nibbles on the females fin.**

Top, right: **nurse sharks copulating.**

Center: **a shark mating circle (males chasing females).**

Bottom: **a close-up of sharks copulating showing the reproductive organs.**

JC/Seapics.com

NR/Seapics.com

MS/Seapics.com

JC/Seapics.com

DP/Seapics.com

Hammerhead Sharks

(Family Sphyrnidae)

The name is truly appropriate. The unique anvil-shaped head distinguishes this family of sharks from all others. Hammerheads are common sharks, with four species in Florida. The common, or smooth ham-merhead is only a winter visitor since it requires cooler water.

The scalloped hammerhead is Florida's most common large hammerhead. It gets its name from the leading edge of its head, which is scalloped or rounded.

The bonnethead is a small inshore shark with a shovel-shaped head. It often congregates in schools, feeding on crabs, mollusks, and small fish.

Larger hammerheads feed mostly on fish, squid, rays, and other sharks, including other hammerheads. The great hammerhead is the largest in Florida and has attacked humans. Hammerheads give birth to live young, and litters may include as many as 37 young sharks.

***Top:* a scalloped hammerhead.**

***Right:* a bonnethead shark.**

***Below:* a great hammerhead. Many hammerheads are large enough to be dangerous, although the bonnethead is not.**

DP/Seapics.com

GA/Seapics.com

BENEFITS OF THE HAMMER-SHAPED HEAD

Scientists disagree about the benefits of the hammerhead's oddly-shaped head. Some argue the shape adds balance to the fish's body, which lacks keels along the edge of the tail, and has rather short pectoral fins. Others theorize the hammer improves the shark's maneuverability when it chases fish. Still others suggest it helps in disturbing food organisms on the sea floor. Whatever the benefits, the unusual shape of the head places the eyes of a large hammerhead as much as 36 inches apart. This distinctive head shape may give the hammerhead a wider angle of view and better depth perception than other sharks.

Variably Shaped Mackerel Sharks

Sand Tigers

(Family Odontaspididae)

Fairly large and snaggle-toothed, the sand tiger shark is rare in Florida but relatively common to the north. This shark tends to be rather sluggish and is not considered dangerous to people, unlike other members of this family. These sharks often feed in groups of three or four, herding and preying upon schools of fish.

Female sand tiger sharks bear only one or two live young, but it's not for lack of trying. These two fetuses simply eat the additional eggs their mother produces. Apparently, their diet agrees with them. At birth, these sharks measure a little more than three feet long.

Top, and right: **the sand tiger moves from the cooler waters of the US East Coast to the warmer Florida waters during cold months. Despite its extremely fierce appearance, this shark is rarely implicated in attacks on humans in this part of the world.**

SHARKS VS. SKATES AND RAYS

All sharks have five to seven gill slits on each side of the head. Most have several rows of pointed teeth, actually highly modified scales. One row of teeth is used at a time. When a tooth becomes worn or breaks off, a tooth in the next row moves forward to replace it. Sharks differ from sawfishes, skates, and rays (collectively known as batoids) in that their gills are on the sides of the head rather than on the ventral portion of the body, and pectoral fins are not attached to gill openings. In batoids, pectoral fins adjoin the head and form a generally flat, plate-shaped body.

Contrary to Hollywood myth, sharks aren't eating machines. In fact, they digest their meals very slowly, sometimes over several days, and may not eat but every second or third day. That may be one reason sharks mature so slowly.

HH/Seapics.com

Basking Sharks
(Family Cetorhinidae)

Second only to whale sharks in size, the basking shark often reaches a length of 30 to 35 feet. There is one temperate species worldwide, and during winter, it migrates into Florida's offshore waters. Basking sharks feed exclusively on plankton near the surface of open sea. A fine meshwork of gill rakers in the throat strains plankton from water flowing into the mouth and out its gills. As their name implies, basking sharks spend a good portion of their time floating or swimming slowly at the ocean's surface. It is surprising that these laid-back, non-aggressive sharks are closely related to the dangerous lamnid sharks, including the great white and mako.

Top: **a basking shark feeding. The gill arches, which strain plankton from the water, are visible in this photo.**

Angel Sharks
(Family Squatinidae)

Angel sharks are flattened, ray-like fishes. The Atlantic angel shark is the only species verified in Florida. This peculiar shark often buries itself like a ray where it can remain camouflaged to ambush an approaching bottom-dwelling fish or invertebrate. Angel sharks get their name from long, wide pectoral fins that look like wings. Unlike the same fins in rays, the front margins of these fins are not connected to the head, which enhances the wing-like appearance.

Dogfish Sharks
(Family Squalidae)

The dogfishes are a family of mostly small, generally deep-water sharks, but three species occur in shallow Florida waters. The Cuban dogfish is the most common and harmless to humans. It congregates in dense schools and feeds on small fishes and invertebrates. The livers of Cuban dogfish are used to produce oils and vitamins.

Much rarer in Florida is the spiny dogfish, which is quite common in other parts of the world. It usually inhabits cooler waters than those found in Florida. Ironically, this species may be the most familiar to people since it is commonly used for dissecting in college anatomy courses. Some deep water dogfishes off Florida are luminescent.

Characteristics of the dogfish include: no anal fin and a hard, curved, pointed spine at the beginning of each dorsal fin.

Thresher Sharks
(Family Alopiidae)

Two species of thresher sharks, the thresher and bigeye thresher, are found in Florida's offshore waters. Their enormous sickle-shaped tails often measure more than half their length and distinguish threshers from other sharks. Their tails dwarf even the babies, which measure almost five feet at birth. Threshers use tails to herd, and possibly stun, fish and squid. Threshers pose no risk to near-shore swimmers, but some believe they may prey on victims of maritime disasters.

AN/Seapics.com

Mackerel Sharks

(Family Lamnidae)

Mackerel sharks are large, voracious feeders known to attack humans. Many boaters and swimmers are happy to learn these sharks are not common in Florida waters, and only three species are found in this state.

The great white shark grows to nearly 20 feet in length and is renowned as the most dangerous shark in the world. Its powerful, super-predatory nature places the great white at the top of the marine food chain where it feeds on seals, dolphins, and other large prey, even other sharks. Recent research, however, suggests these sharks are more picky in eating habits than previously thought. The young of the great white take more than 10 years to mature, so this species is vulnerable to over-harvesting despite its fierce reputation.

The shortfin mako shark is smaller and considered less dangerous than the great white. Makos are famous for leaping from the water while chasing prey or when hooked. Sometimes mako meat is marketed as swordfish.

DH/Seapics.com

Top: **the great white shark. Tours are available in some places such as Baja California which allow the adventurous to observe great whites underwater from the safety of steel cages. Note the typical triangular-shaped teeth.**
Above: **another view of a great white. This is the most dangerous of all sharks, but fortunately it is not common in Florida waters. A key difference between the great white and other sharks is that the upper lobe of the tail is the same length as the lower lobe, instead of being noticeably longer.**

Electric Rays

(Family Narcinidae)

Electric rays once were lumped into the same family as torpedo rays. The lesser electric ray is the only member of this family in Florida. It is common in inshore waters of the Gulf and often can be found in the surf zone. Similar to torpedos, electric rays can deliver enough of a charge to disable a sensitive person, as much as 37 volts. Electric rays eat primarily bottom-dwelling invertebrates such as crabs and shrimps.

All electric rays are ovoviviparous, delivering up to 15 live young, following a gestation period of eight to ten months. Late in their development, the young receive from their mothers a protein-rich secretion called "uterine milk."

Top and below: **lesser electric ray.**

DP/Seapics.com

JM/Seapics.com

Torpedo Rays

(Family Torpedinidae)

Torpedos have electric organs (large specialized muscles) on either side of their bodies behind the eyes. These organs can deliver over 200 volts, enough to stun an adult human. More often, of course, electrical charges repel predators, stun prey, and receive information about their surrounding environment, much like bats use their "sonar" to identify their surroundings.

All torpedo rays are sluggish bottom-dwellers, occupying inshore waters out to the continental slope. To catch small fishes and crustaceans, torpedos bury themselves in the substrate and stun unsuspecting prey that pass by. Only one species is found in Florida, the Atlantic torpedo.

ELECTRICITY IN RAYS AND SKATES

Even human bodies crackle with electricity. People just don't feel it. However, certain ray species can shock the largest of humans. Electric organs in these rays are located on either side of the body disc behind the eyes and can generate quite a charge, as much as 200 volts or more. These kidney-shaped organs are composed of "electroplaques" that produce the shock.

All electric rays are sluggish bottom-dwellers. They conceal themselves beneath sediment and wait for unsuspecting prey to come close. Then zap! Stunned prey are easily captured. A ray's electric charge may also be used in self-defense, for example, when a diver ventures too close.

Electric skates possess weaker electrogenic organs that produce a lesser charge. These skates may use electrical discharges to confuse predators.

Sawfishes

Sawfishes

(Family Pristidae)

Sawfishes are shark-like rays named for a long, flattened "snout" studded with sharp, tooth-like projections on each side. The scientific term for this snout is "rostral process," but most people just call it a "saw." The saw is used to stir up bottom sand and mud in search of food and to slash through schools of fish to kill or stun prey.

The two species once common in Florida have rarely been found in recent years. The largetooth sawfish has relatively few (but large) teeth on its saw. In contrast, the smalltooth sawfish has many relatively small teeth. Both are found in estuaries and even enter fresh water at times.

Sawfishes are live bearers. The difficulty of giving birth to a baby with a saw on its head has been solved rather well. The saw on pups is flexible, and the teeth are soft. Once the pup is born, these structures firm up, and the baby sawfish swims on its way.

DP/Seapics.com

Right: **a smalltooth sawfish. This species has a longer blade with 24 or more teeth. The largetooth sawfish, by comparison, has a shorter blade with 20 or less teeth. Both species are now rarely seen because they easily tangle in fishing nets and fishermen have killed large numbers of them through the years.**

Guitarfishes and Skates

Guitarfishes

(Family Rhinobatidae)

The Atlantic guitarfish is the only representative of this family in Florida. The name is rather descriptive. The nearly round body disk so common in rays is absent in guitarfish. Instead, the body is slender with a flattened, pointed snout. Guitarfish don't "fly" through the water like rays; rather, they swim like sharks. Inshore bottom-dwellers, guitarfish eat primarily small mollusks and crustaceans which they capture by suction and crush with their small, rounded teeth.

MB/Seapics.com

Right: **an Atlantic guitarfish. This is a moderately common and harmless species found in shallow to moderately deep waters off Florida.**

Skates

(Family Rajidae)

Skates are the deep-water rays. They are small and look much like stingrays. However, skates lack the stingrays' tail spine and have well-developed dorsal and caudal fins. Most skates live near the bottom, and various species range from the shallow estuaries to the deep-sea floor. Most skates feed primarily on bottom-dwelling invertebrates, such as crabs, worms, and shrimps; some species also eat small fishes.

As a group, skates are rather poorly known. Of the 200 or so species worldwide, perhaps eleven occur in Florida. Other deep water species may dwell offshore. Nearshore species commonly seen include the clearnose and roundel skates.

Male skates possess specialized patches of thorns on their outer disk, used to grip females during copulation. Skates are oviparous and encase their eggs in tough pouches. Many a beachgoer has found these "mermaids' purses" washed up on the sand at low tide.

PC/Seapics.com

Devilrays, Cownose, and Eagle Rays

Stingrays

(Family Dasyatidae)

What separates a veteran Florida beachgoer from a first-timer? The "stingray shuffle." Experienced swimmers don't pick up their feet and put 'em down. They shuffle through shallow water. Rays are shy creatures and usually get out of the way of humans if given a chance.

Depending on the species, stingrays may possess on their tails one to many serrated spines (actually modified scales). These contain grooves that can deliver a toxin able to inflict an extremely painful wound that may become infected.

Most stingrays dwell on the bottom, or maybe that should be *in* the bottom. They usually bury themselves with just their eyes and their respiratory holes (spiracles) exposed. As stingrays land on the bottom, they fan the sand with pectoral fins, and let the sand fall on their backs. Here they lie in wait for their invertebrate prey. Stingrays are ovoviviparous and nourish developing young with a secretion from filaments in the wall of the uterus.

Bottom: **a yellow stingray.**

DP/Seapics.com

Round Stingrays

(Family Urolophidae)

As their name implies, round stingrays possess rounded disks. In fact, in silhouette, they look much like frying pans. They also carry a doubly serrate, venomous spine near the base of the tail. The yellow stingray is the only member of this family in Florida and is common near shore. Yellow stingrays live in sandy areas near beaches and coral reefs. They are found from North Carolina to South America. They are among the smaller rays, and as their name suggests, their skin is yellowish.

DP/Seapics.com

DP/Seapics.com

Top: a group of migrating cownose rays. Cownose rays are often seen around the Gulf Coast along the beaches and in estuaries. Curious creatures, they have been known to swim close to the shore line and gaze up at humans. Cownose rays sometimes gather in concentrations of up to 10,000. In the fall, they migrate from Florida to Mexico, especially the Yucatan Peninsula. Cownose rays are found throughout the Gulf of Mexico.

Middle and bottom: The southern stingray shown in both these photos is probably the stingray most familiar to Floridians. In the middle photo, it is burying itself in the sand, or possibly stirring up food. The Atlantic stingray is another common inshore ray and, together with the southern stingray, gives a good reason to do the stingray shuffle. Other Florida species include the roughtail stingray and bluntnose stingray.

DP/Seapics.com

THE STINGRAY'S STING

Stingrays aren't aggressive toward people, but injuries from stingrays are still common. Usually, injuries result from an unwary wader stepping on or brushing against a stingray half buried in sand, and the ray reacting reflexively by popping up its tail and jabbing its stinger into the victim's foot or lower leg.

The tail contains one or more barbed stingers with two grooves encased in a sheath. The grooves convey a fairly powerful nerve toxin from venom glands. The stinger leaves a deep, jagged laceration, and the stinger apparatus injects its protein-based toxin into the wound, causing immediate, intense pain. Sometimes envenomation doesn't occur, most likely because the stingray has lost or torn the sheath covering the stinger apparatus. Still the wound is painful and usually bleeds freely. Part of the stinger may break off in the wound. The serrations point toward the base of the spine, making its removal somewhat difficult.

The stingrays' toxin can affect the human heart. Fortunately, the toxin is very sensitive to heat. Soaking the wound in water as hot as the victim can stand causes the toxin to break down and reduces the pain from the wound. Perhaps the key word here is "reduces." It is far better to avoid the experience by learning the "stingray shuffle."

DP/Seapics.com

Eagle Rays
(Family Myliobatidae)

The calm of a warm summer day is suddenly shattered by a noisy splash behind the boat. There it is again; hardly fifty feet away, a large ray leaps. Only the back of this ray isn't gray. It's covered with round white spots—a spectacular sight, indeed, as a spotted eagle ray makes its debut.

Eagle rays have eyes on the sides of the head rather than on top, as with stingrays. On their long tails, most eagle rays possess one or more doubly serrate, venomous spines capable of making a painful wound.

The spotted eagle ray sometimes travels in small schools and feeds mainly on bivalve mollusks, which it crushes with tile-like teeth. The cownose ray sometimes congregates in schools of several hundred. It eats mostly lobsters, crabs, and mollusks.

***Top:* a bullnose ray. Note that in comparison with the manta, the mouth of the bullnose ray is entirely on the underside of the fish.**

***Bottom:* a spotted eagle ray.**

TC/Seapics.com

DP/Seapics.com

Mantas (devil rays)

Adult mantas usually remain farther offshore than others of this family, though young mantas often patrol inshore bays and beaches. Mantas are the largest rays, approaching 22 feet in width, and weighing over a ton. Mantas lack a venomous spine, but if captured, they can still inflict injury due to their size and strength.

Mantas often congregate in large schools and usually live near the surface of open coastal waters. There they may be seen at quite a distance because of their habit of curling the tips of their pectoral fins, or "wings," up out of the water. Mantas also make spectacular leaps, splashing down flat with lots of spray and noise. As plankton feeders, they strain tiny organisms from water that passes through sieve-like plates on their gills. Mantas sport a pair of lobes at the front of the head on either side of the mouth. These cephalic fins may serve to direct water, as well as small fishes, into the manta's mouth as they "fly" through the water with graceful flaps of their wing-like pectorals.

MU/Seapics.com

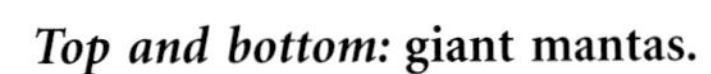

Top and bottom: **giant mantas.**

WNR

Sturgeons

(Family Acipenseridae)

English kings once decreed sturgeons to be royal fish and even today they are considered to be the property of the queen. Even a museum must obtain royal consent to add a specimen to their collection. Sturgeon eggs still fetch a high price. However, they swim now in only a remnant of the range they once occupied, and their numbers have dwindled to endangered status in some species.

Sturgeons grow large and live long. However, the species found in the US and Asia is smaller than its European relatives. Sturgeons take a long time, perhaps eight years or more, to mature sexually. Even then, sturgeons don't spawn every year. A female may take three or four years to build up enough eggs to spawn. Many sturgeons are anadromous, spawning in fresh water but living much of their lives in the ocean.

Two species are found in Florida. The Atlantic sturgeon is the larger of the two, growing up to 14 feet long. Two distinct subspecies exist, one on the Atlantic coast and one on the Gulf coast. The Gulf population spawns primarily in the Suwannee River today. They are also plentiful in the Yellow River System of the Panhandle. They once used the Apalachicola River, but a dam now blocks upriver migration.

The shortnose sturgeon is a rare Atlantic coast fish and grows three to four feet long. Both it and the Atlantic sturgeon may have spawned in the Ocklawaha River before Rodman Dam was built. Water velocity is critical to these sturgeons' spawning success. When there is too much current, eggs can't adhere to the substrate. Too low a velocity allows the eggs to clump, resulting in increased mortality. In the early stages of their life, sturgeons have an adhesive they use to attach themselves to the river bottom.

Perhaps no more than 3,000 sturgeon remain in Florida, mostly in the vicinity of the Suwannee River.

***Top:* the Gulf of Mexico subspecies of the Atlantic sturgeon. These prehistoric fish have a mouth which can be extended for vacuuming small creatures off the bottom.**

CAVIAR, THE FOOD OF KINGS

Caviar, a product of sturgeon eggs, never has been eaten much by common folk. It has always cost too much. Caviar can run about $300 a pound. This has resulted in great value being placed on sturgeons, perhaps to their detriment. Sturgeons produce lots of eggs if given the chance, but sometimes they get only one chance because they are hunted so intensely. Fishermen extract sturgeon eggs by dissecting dead females, or they strip eggs from living sturgeon and return the fish to the water in hopes they will produce more eggs.

Caviar is prepared by lightly salting the eggs to cause water to be drawn from them. Then the eggs are drained and packaged. Value is a function of salting, it seems. Lightly salted, almost liquid caviar usually fetches the highest price.

How are the dead sturgeons used? Many people prize smoked sturgeon meat, and fine oil is processed from sturgeons. A sturgeon's most valued body part, however, is its swim bladder. A sheet of almost pure gelatin, called isinglass, is processed from sturgeons' swim bladders. Isinglass is used to make special glues and similar products, and to clarify white wines.

DM/Seapics.com

Gars

(Order Lepisosteiformes)

Gars

(Family Lepisosteidae)

Gars are easy to recognized because of their long, toothy jaws. These living fossils were once found in Europe, India, Africa, and South America. For unknown reasons, gars died. Today, they are restricted to eastern North America south to Costa Rica and Cuba. Gars live primarily in fresh water but are highly tolerant of salt water.

Gars are found in lowland rivers, lakes, sloughs, swamps, and canals where they often congregate just below the water's surface. Gars thrive in water bodies that suffer periods of low dissolved oxygen when many other fishes die. They can do this because of their unique swim bladder, which is connected to the esophagus and works much like a lung when air is swallowed. Even when there is no shortage of oxygen in the water, gars rise to the surface and gulp air. Gars drown when denied the opportunity to "breathe" air.

Spawning in gars is a tumultuous affair. Usually several males accompany a female into a weedy area. There, amidst much thrashing, the adhesive eggs are deposited and fertilized. Upon hatching, the larvae attach to submerged objects with an adhesive pad on their lower jaw and remain there until their yolk sac is absorbed. Then they begin their predatory lives, feeding first on plankton, then on larger prey as they grow—including one another. As adults, they feed primarily on small fishes.

Alligator gars reach up to ten feet in length and once populated sluggish water bodies along most of the Gulf Coast. No one knows why, but the alligator gar disappeared from all of its original range in Florida except for the western Panhandle. Even there, it is rarely seen. Alligator gars add water birds and other aquatic animals to their diet of fish.

The longnose gar lives up to its name. Its narrow snout is more than twice as long as the rest of its head. This gar prefers moving water and is found in rivers more than stagnant backwaters. It grows up to six feet in length.

Florida's most common gar is simply named the Florida gar. This gar is found throughout the state in slow-moving or stagnant waters. It is also Florida's smallest gar, topping out at four feet.

Top: **a longnose gar.**

Below: **a juvenile Florida gar. This gar is foundin peninsular Florida west to the Ochlockonee River.**

Bottom: **a spotted gar. It is found in the Appalachicola River and in the Panhandle drainage.**

VU - PC

VU - R&AS

Bowfin

(Family Amiidae)

North America can claim the only living species of bowfin in the world, and it lives throughout Florida. *Amia calva* has both gills and a functional lung, much like gars. Bowfins are aggressive carnivores, feeding on a variety of fishes, frogs, and other animals small enough to fit into its rather large, toothy mouth.

The bowfin's aggressive nature extends to courtship. Mating occurs in weedy shallows. Males, often in a group, construct circular nests among roots or other structure. When a female approaches, the male responds with nose bites and nudges, and he will even chase the female to continue this mating behavior. When at last the female lies in the nest, the male comes alongside her, and eggs are laid and fertilized. More than one couple may use the same nest, and the male may try to mate with other females. What the male may lack as a suitor, he makes up for as a parent. Once the eggs hatch, the fry school together, and the male boldly guards them and the nest. Once the fry have grown beyond the need for parental care, the adult bowfin returns to his solitary life.

VU - GM

Above and center: **a bowfin. A "living fossil," and the only living species of an ancient family of fishes once found throughout much of the world. Bowfins are known from Jurassic fossil deposits dating back 150 million year.s**

DP/Seapics.com

ELOPOMORPHS

The superorder Elopomorpha is comprised of four orders of fishes that bear little resemblance to one another as adults. These include large silvery tarpons and small silvery eels. While these species look nothing alike as adults, they closely resemble each other as larvae. This is their connection. The larva, called a leptocephalus (meaning "thin head"), drifts on open ocean currents as a transparent, ribbon-like creature. Eventually, it drops to the ocean floor, shrinks, and transforms into a miniature version of an adult.

Tarpons and Ladyfishes

(Order Elopiformes)

Ladyfishes

(Family Elopidae)

The ladyfish inhabits Florida's shallow coastal waters and even enters fresh water, in particular the St. Johns River. These slender fish migrate in part of their range to escape cooling water. Ladyfish are thought to spawn in open ocean, and their leptocephali enter estuaries to mature.

Ladyfish are also known as "ten-pounders." This name apparently arose from their ability to fight with anglers, not their size. "Threepounder" would be more accurate.

Florida may actually be home to two forms of ladyfish, northern and southern. Both forms are virtually indistinguishable except for differences in the number of vertebrae in adults and in the musculature of the larvae. If these differences are sufficiently confirmed, the southern form may be named a new species.

VU - FR

Above: **a ladyfish (juvenile). A sleek, fast-swimming fish that is common in estuaries and the lower parts of some of the larger Florida rivers.**

THREATS TO FLORIDA'S FISHES

Florida's diverse aquatic habitats are susceptible to diverse environmental problems, including coastal and wetland development, pollution, and destructive fishing practices.

Often restricted to limited habitats such as ponds, streams, or coral reefs, fishes are susceptible to environmental changes. Not all changes are necessarily bad, nor are all changes caused by human impact. Natural aquatic systems are subject to natural fluctuations in water level and quality, dissolved oxygen content, and water temperature, among other factors. Weather patterns can help or hurt fish populations. Sudden cold snaps during the winter kill large numbers of tropical coastal species, such as sheepshead and snook. Cloudy days following heavy rainfall team up to create oxygen shortages in ponds and streams that leave many largemouth bass and other sunfishes dead in their wake. On the other hand, periodic drying of some ponds and lake margins restores fertility to these areas and produces more productive water bodies when the normal water level returns. Florida is famous for hurricanes, and these storms can wreak havoc on shallow reefs and coastal wetlands.

The greatest threats to Florida's fishes, however, come by way of permanent habitat destruction. Florida's development patterns greatly impact the state's aquatic ecosystems. Traveling around Florida's coasts will reveal housing and commercial developments where mangroves and sea grasses once thrived. Shorelines in these areas are hardened with vertical sea walls, and storm-water systems channel nutrient-laden runoff into rivers and bays, thus reducing water quality. The cumulative impact of such development have been disastrous, at times. For instance, an important clam and oyster fishery in Tampa Bay collapsed as the bay and its surrounding area were developed.

Some aquatic habitats are especially fragile. Coral reefs, for example, grow at an agonizingly slow pace. Pollution and runoff from activities on land can smother reefs with sediment or introduce nutrients that stimulate prolific algal growth that can smother corals. Boat anchors break the brittle corals, and ships grounding on the reefs can and do damage to extensive portions of reefs.

Dredging often destroys extensive areas of fish habitat, and not just at the coast. Dredging in the Apalachicola River permits barge traffic but covers fishery habitat with sand and removes snags and other structure important to many river fishes, such as the uncommon shoal bass. It also generates siltation downstream.

Storm-water runoff dumps huge loads of nutrients and heavy metals into receiving waters. High nutrient levels stimulate prolific blooms of algae that increase eutrophication in ponds and lakes. Heavy metals, such as mercury, accumulate in sediments and concentrate as they pass upward in the food chain to the point that in some water bodies top-level predators, such as largemouth bass, may contain levels high enough to be unsafe to eat.

Florida's springs are usually regarded as pristine habitats, and the general perception is that they are free of the contaminants and problems affecting surface waters. While spring waters are still crystal clear, excess nutrients carried down from the surface have, in recent years, been entering the aquifer in ever-increasing quantities. These nutrients promote algal growth, which has served in many cases to choke off the higher aquatic plants that are characteristic of Florida springs. In Manatee Springs, manatees have long fed on this vegetation, which has resulted in these plants being cropped back close their base at certain times of the year. Under normal circumstances, the plants would quickly grow back. However, today, this re-growth is impeded by a layer of algae created by the excess nutrients in the water.

MERCURY IN FLORIDA'S FISHES

Concern about heavy metals concentrations in Florida water bodies has been increasing for years. Mercury, especially, has generated keen interest due to the toxic effects in people who consume it through fish. The problem isn't new. In the 1950s, 131 people in Minamata, Japan suffered a variety of unusual symptoms—progressive blindness, deafness, lack of coordination, and intellectual deterioration. Forty-six died. Investigators eventually learned a factory was discharging trace amounts of mercuric chloride in its effluent into Minamata Bay. However, this discharge alone could not account for such extensive illness. Surprisingly, the culprit turned out to be the bay's ecosystem, itself. Microorganisms in the bay's sediments were converting the mercuric chloride to methyl mercury, a potent neurotoxin.

Methyl mercury is absorbed into the blood, then distributed throughout the body. It also passes into the brain and, finally, reaches nerve cells. Methyl mercury interferes with the way nerve cells function, thus producing a variety of symptoms associated with nerve damage.

Mercury occurs naturally in the environment, but mercury compounds also are released by burning household and industrial waste, as well as, fossil fuels. Mercury in the air condenses on tiny particles and returns to the earth in precipitation. Elemental mercury really isn't much of a problem in itself. Humans absorb only about .01%, and small amounts of mercury are usually safely eliminated. The problem with mercury is twofold, both the form and the amount absorbed.

Metals, including mercury, tend to accumulate in sediments and, for the most part, don't biodegrade. Anaerobic bacteria convert mercury to methyl mercury. Algae and other microorganisms absorb methyl mercury and are consumed by plankton-feeding fishes and invertebrates. Larger predatory fishes then consume these smaller fishes and invertebrates. Fish also can absorb methyl mercury through their gills. Thus methyl mercury is concentrated as it passes upward in the food chain, a process known as bioaccumulation. Almost all mercury in fish is in the form of methyl mercury. The methyl mercury is tightly bound to proteins in fish tissues, unaffected by cleaning and cooking. To make matters worse, almost all methyl mercury humans consume with the fish tissue can be absorbed.

Elevated levels of mercury in Florida fish were discovered in the Everglades in 1989. Since then, the state has identified significant problems with mercury and issued health advisories restricting the consumption of largemouth bass and other gamefish in more than two million acres of the Everglades and Big Cypress. In 1995, a limited consumption advisory for Jack crevalle, spotted seatrout, and gafftopsail catfish was initiated in Florida Bay. Mercury has been detected at levels of concern in largemouth bass throughout Florida. In 1998, largemouth bass and bowfin were found to have the highest levels of mercury reported in gamefish in Florida.

Is it time to run for cover when someone offers a Florida seafood supper? Of course not. Even fishermen eat relatively small amounts of the species most affected. A call to the Florida Department of Environmental Protection, Florida Fish and Wildlife Conservation Commission, and/or local health department will reveal which water bodies and species of fish are most affected in a specific location.

DP/Seapics.com

Tarpons

(Family Megalopidae)

Only two species of tarpon are recognized worldwide. One, *Megalops atlanticus*, occurs in Florida.

Tarpon breed in salt water but can survive equally well in either a marine or freshwater environment. In fact, tarpon inhabit a broad range of habitats, from sand and sea-grass beds to coral reefs. They grow to seven or more feet in length and may weigh over 200 pounds. A tarpon can survive in oxygen-poor water because its swim bladder is modified into a lung-like organ that enables it to come to the surface and breathe air.

Tarpon take fruitfulness to an extreme. One female about six feet long was found to be carrying more than 12 million eggs. They spawn offshore near the continental shelf from May through July, often during a dark moon phase, and this timing may offer a measure of protection to the eggs. Apparently, nuptial activity frequently involves a "daisy chain," where the nose of one fish follows at the tail of another as they swim in a circle. Very young tarpon enter estuaries to mature and may roam far upstream in tidal creeks and canals. They mature in seven to 13 years, and then join the ocean-going adults.

Fortunately, tarpon aren't in much danger of being over fished, despite being a popular and spectacular sport fish. Tarpon aren't considered food fish. A pemit to keep a tarpon to mount costs $50. Consequently, few tarpon are caught and killed by anglers in Florida.

THE TARPON ROLL

Tarpon often congregate in large numbers in pursuit of fish and frequently break the surface in a distinctive roll. Rolling behavior appears to be a means to gulp air. Tarpon possess an air bladder that helps them survive in oxygen-depleted water. This feature of tarpons especially aids survival of juveniles. Young tarpon grow up in shallow estuaries, tidal creeks, and tidal ponds where oxygen depletion is common.

A tarpon's rolling becomes less frequent as the water's oxygen content increases. Nevertheless, tarpon need atmospheric oxygen. They die within hours when denied the opportunity to come to the surface and gulp air, even in highly oxygenated water.

MU/Seapics.com

ARE THERE TARPON AT TARPON SPRINGS?

There are, at least during the summer. Tarpon are sensitive to cold temperatures and migrate to warmer regions as water temperature drops. Many sources credit Mary Ormond Boyer with giving Tarpon Springs its name due to the abundance of tarpon (and springs) in the area. Of course, that was very early in the town's history, probably in the late 1870's. Today, Tarpons Springs is better known for its Greek restaurants and its sponge industry. Boca Grande is now more commonly identified with tarpon fishing.

Right: **a captured tarpon is walked through the water to prepare it to be released. This photo, and the one below, shows clearly why the tarpon is called the "silver king."**

MU/Seapics.com

N&LR

WS/Seapics.com

TARPON MADNESS

Tarpon often congregate in large numbers as they pursue schools of mullet or other prey. A tarpon may grow to over eight feet in length and weigh around 350 pounds. For these reasons they are called the "Silver Kings" of Florida's gamefish.

The tarpon's reputation does not stem from it table quality. Its flesh is coarse and bony. But a tarpon makes a challenging target for an angler. A tarpon is a powerfull swimmer and makes spectacular leaps when hooked, enticing some visitors to come to Florida just for the tarpon fishing. During the warm months, tarpon may be encountered anywhere along Florida's coasts. But the best tarpon fishing is in the southern half of the state.

It is hard to tell just how much money tarpon fishing brings to Florida. It may be a considerable sum. In just one tournament, the 2001 World's Richest Tarpon Tournament in Boca Grande, the prize money totalled over $250,000. The entry fee was $5,200.

WS/Seapics.com

Bonefishes

(Family Albulidae)

A bonefish is just that—bony. Currently, one species is recognized in Florida, with possibly another species in deeper water. Florida's bonefish frequents shallow marine grass flats, where it probes the bottom, head down, for shrimp, crabs, and snails. In very shallow water, its tail sometimes sticks up into the air from this feeding posture. Though juveniles have been collected in the Panhandle, bonefish in Florida more often remain along the southern part of the peninsula and throughout the Keys.

The speedy bonefish is translucent (it is actually possible to see through its fins), and thus difficult to spot against a sandy bottom. Bonefish have been called "ghostly" and "spooky" because of the way they blend into their environment. Fishermen watch in frustration as their image appears and disappears in the water. This factor, plus the fish's ferocious fighting spirit, makes the bonefish an irresistible challenge for many sport fishermen, and has created a mini-industry in South Florida. Although bonefish are tasty, because of their boniness many fishermen prefer to take a photo, and then release their prey to fight again.

WS/Seapics.com

Top and bottom: **views of bonefish. Bonefish are found in shallow, sandy-bottomed flats close to shore.**

True Eels

Freshwater Eels

(Family Anguillidae)

Freshwater eels are unique among eels in that they are catadromous; they spend most of their adult lives in fresh water and return to the sea to spawn. In general, males remain in the brackish estuaries near the coast, while females move farther upstream into freshwater areas. Of 16 species worldwide, only one occurs in Florida.

American eels are most often thought of as freshwater fish since they are more frequently encountered in freshwater. Those eels are females, of course, since males remain closer to the coast. Both sexes may live up to fifteen years in their respective waters. Eventually, American eels migrate downstream to the ocean and continue their journey to the Sargasso Sea (see box on this page) to spawn once and die.

The blood of both American and European eels and a few other eels contains a poison. Eel gourmets need not worry, however, since cooking destroys the poison.

Although freshwater eels are a favored food item in Europe, they are seldom used for this purpose in North America. The American eels are just as edible. It is most likely because eels look like snakes. Fear and prejudice against snakes in North America has prevented eels from becoming a popular addition to the dining table.

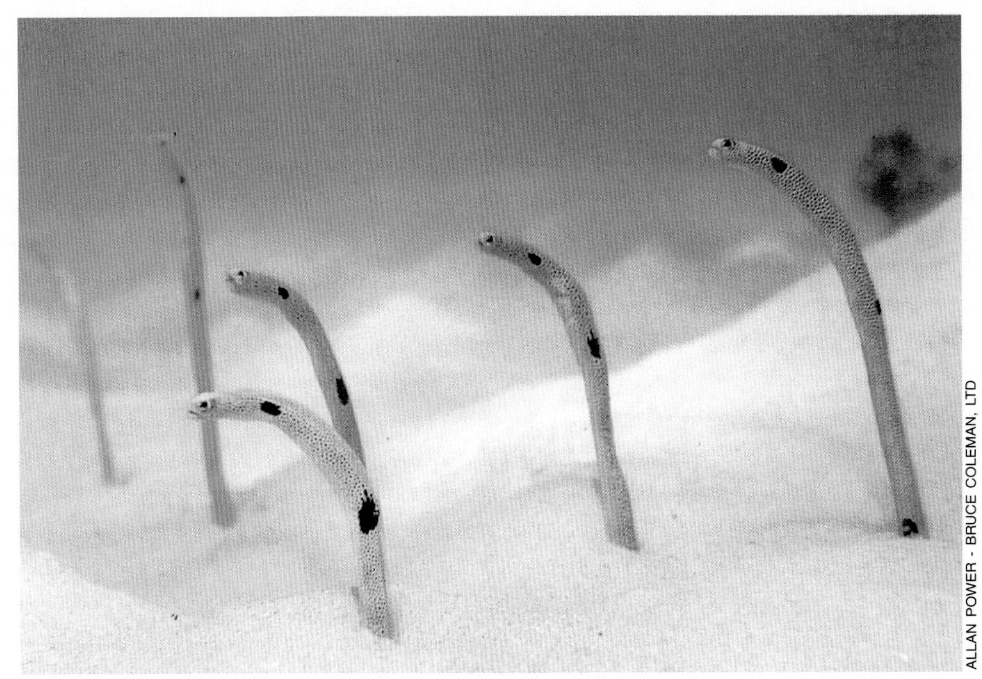

ALLAN POWER - BRUCE COLEMAN, LTD

EEL GARDENS

Garden eels came by their common name as the result of observations by Dr. William Beebe, an American scientist who pioneered studies in the deep ocean using his bathysphere. He once saw a "swaying garden of eels" in the Gulf of California. The name fits rather well. Garden eels live in dense colonies throughout most of the world's tropical seas, embedded in the sand like blades of grass.

During the day, garden eels extend about halfway out of burrows, swaying in the current to catch plankton and debris. They range in depths from three feet to over 1000 feet. Garden eels dig burrows tail-first and line them with mucus derived from body secretions. These fish are perfectly adapted to the lifestyle they lead. They have enlarged eyes and binocular vision. They also possess specialized tail tips that enable them to dig holes.

Garden eels mate by entwining their heads and slender bodies outside their burrows while keeping their tails firmly anchored inside. The larvae drift with the current until they transform. These juveniles burrow into the substrate at the edge of the existing colony, inadvertently helping the colony grow.

BH/Seapics.com

Above: **a manytooth conger eel.**

Conger Eels

(Family Congridae)

Few coastal residents have ever seen a conger eel. Yet, they are among the most common fishes. Like snake eels, conger eels and garden eels find homes in a broad range of habitats, from shallow tidal pools to ocean depths. These eels are most active at night, and life histories of most species are poorly understood. In fact, "conger eel" is commonly applied to several species. Over 115 species live in virtually all tropical and subtropical seas, and Florida may be home to as many as 13. The most visible are the manytooth conger and brown garden eel.

PILGRIMAGE TO THE SARGASSO SEA

American eels live as adults in fresh water but return to salt water to spawn. They return to the Sargasso Sea, a vast area of the Atlantic Ocean southeast of Bermuda. No adults nor eggs have ever been collected there, but the smallest larvae, leptocephali, are found there, and progressively larger larvae are found as one moves closer to the coast. By the time they reach the coast, they have transformed to recognizable eels. Males remain near the coast in estuaries. Females continue upstream into fresh water. Once they reach sexual maturity, females return downstream to the ocean, and males and females migrate to the Sargasso Sea. American eels and European eels spawn in the same sea at about the same time. Yet, somehow, these species separate and each returns to its home shore. Scientists believe american eels die after spawning since no adults return from their spawning grounds.

DP/Seapics.com

Moray Eels

(Family Muraenidae)

Morays are frequently seen by divers around reefs and by viewers of nature shows on television. In both places, morays appear quite menacing. Leering out of dark crevices with toothy mouths agape, morays look ready to lash out at anyone or anything coming too close. The fact that morays have attacked human hands on occasion adds to their fearsome reputation.

They really aren't so mean. Apparently, morays are a bit near-sighted and don't like to be disturbed. Still, caution should be the key around morays. They have powerful jaws, needle-sharp teeth, and can inflict a serious wound. That toothy leer, however, is not really menacing. It is built-in, the same as a pelican's smile. Like other fishes, morays must pump water past gills to breathe. Their gaping mouths, showing wicked-looking teeth, produce a malevolent stare, but they are simply respiring.

When eaten, morays have been known to cause ciguatera poisoning. There may be as many as 200 species of moray eels worldwide, with 18 or so species occurring in Florida. Perhaps the most common Florida moray, the spotted moray is found on shallow reefs and rocky shorelines of eastern and southern Florida. Usually divers see just its head protruding from its hole.

Top: **a diver with a green moray.**

Bottom: **a spotted moray.**

MPO/Seapics.com

"THE ENTRAILS OF THE EARTH"

For centuries, perhaps, people thought eels just happened somehow. Depending on who was expounding on eels at the time, listeners might have heard that eels grew from horses' hair, or from skin scrapings, or the eggs of beetles, or even from the entrails of the earth. This smorgasbord of curious opinions developed from attempts to figure out where eels came from. Eels were always fully-grown adults when people saw them, even the folks who studied them. Then in the late 1700s, someone noticed sexual organs developing in an adult eel. It wasn't until early in the 20th Century, however, that Danish naturalist, Johannes Schmidt, traced returning eel larvae of the genus Anguilla back to the Sargasso Sea, where the adults spawn.

MK/Seapics.com

Top: a goldentail moray.

Middle: a viper moray.

Bottom, left: a chain moray.

Bottom, right: a reticulate moray.

DP/Seapics.com

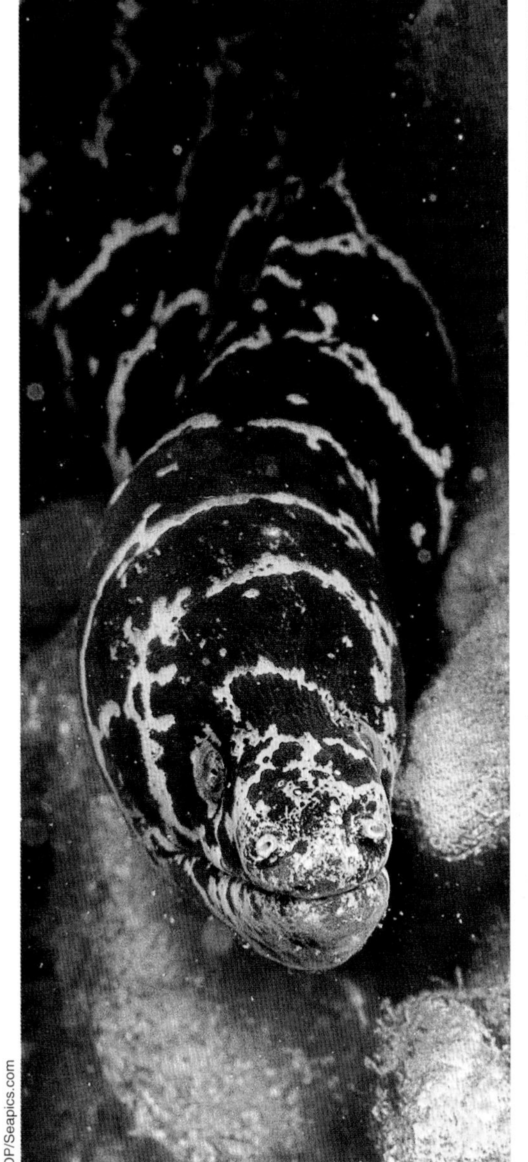

DP/Seapics.com

MK/Seapics.com

DP/Seapics.com

Snake Eels
(Family Ophichthidae)

Snake eels are so named because of spotted or striped markings that mimic patterns of venomous sea snakes. Perhaps these markings confuse or intimidate predators. This is the largest eel family, with close to 260 species. Thirty-two species are reported from eastern US waters, and most can be found in Florida. The ones most likely to be seen in Florida are the spotted spoon-nose eel (*Echiophis intertinctus*), sharptail eel (*Myrichthys breviceps*), goldspotted eel (*Myrichthys ocellatus*), the abundant speckled worm eel (*Myrophis punctatus*), and spotted snake eel (*Ophichthus ophis*).

Snake eels and worm eels occupy a rather wide range of tropical habitats, from shallow intertidal zones to depths over 2000 feet. Most species burrow tail-first in the sand or mud, but some adults swim in the middle depths. They differ in that snake eels possess a hard, pointed, tail without a fin, and worm eels possess a tail fin. Worm eels really do look like worms.

DP/Seapics.com

BH/Seapics.com

MK/Seapics.com

Top: **goldspotted snake eel.**

Middle: **sharptail eel.**

Bottom, left: **spotted eel.**

Bottom, right: **sharptail eel.**

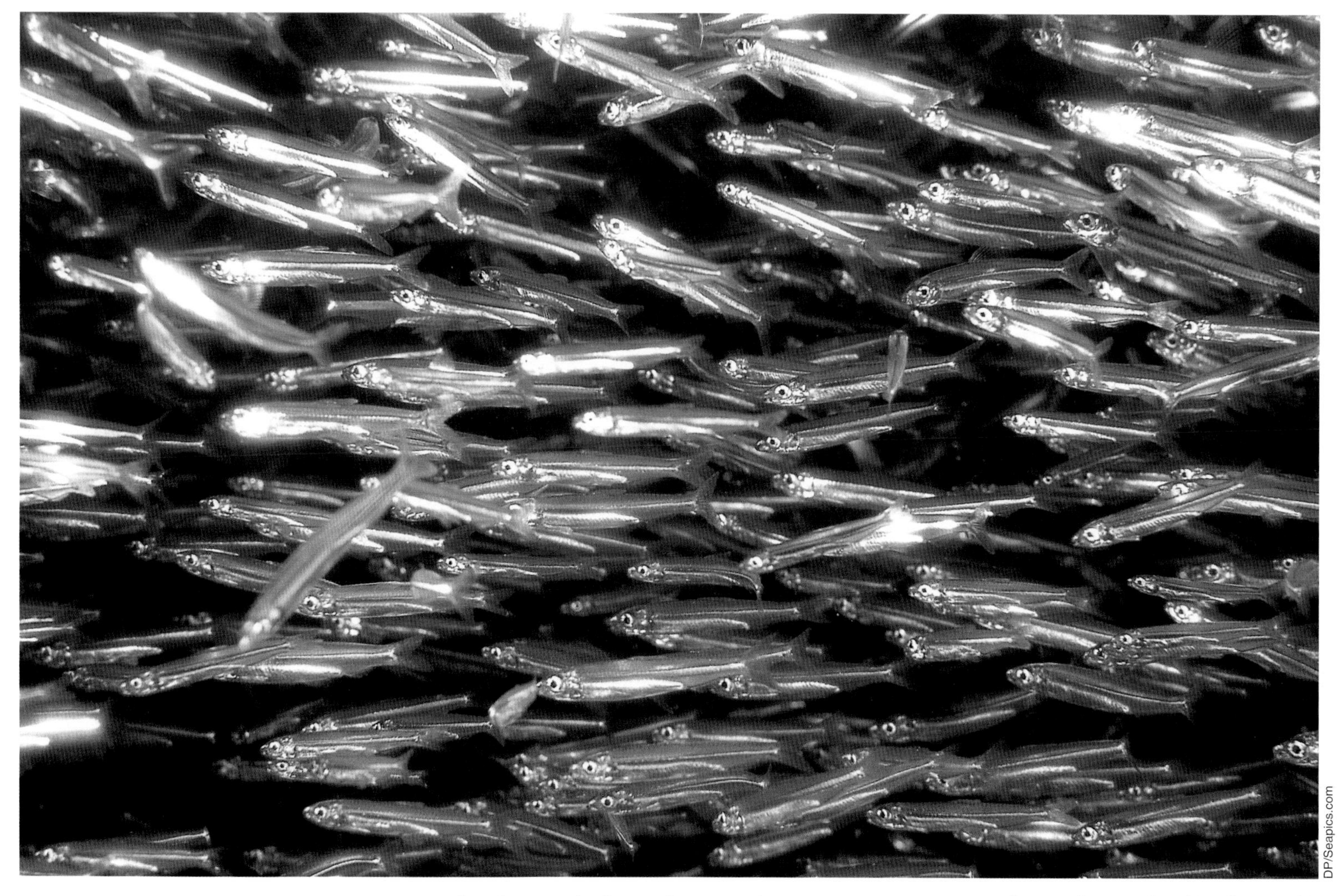

DP/Seapics.com

Anchovies and Herrings

Anchovies

(Family Engraulidae)

Almost everyone has seen anchovies. They come in little cans and adorn pizzas and Caesar salads. However, before they reached the cannery, they swam in immense schools in estuaries and along coastlines. It seems like almost every creature that swims likes to eat anchovies. They are an important prey fish for a vast number of marine animals and a popular bait and food fish for humans. Anchovies are extremely numerous and can withstand heavy commercial fishing pressure. They grow and reproduce quickly and lay huge numbers of eggs. For all their resilience otherwise, anchovies are very fragile. When anchovies are caught in a net, their scales and skin slough off, and they soon die.

Nine species of anchovies live along Florida's coasts, including the striped anchovy and the bay anchovy. Anchovies are filter feeders. They simply open their mouths wide and swim, filtering plankton from water with comb-like gill rakers at the back of the mouth, before the water passes through their gills.

A unique feature of anchovies is their "rostral organ," presumably used for sensory functions yet to be understood. An extensive net-like system of sensory canals on the head extends from the rostral organ over the cheek and behind the eye.

Herrings

(Family Clupeidae)

The herrings, sardines, menhaden, and shads are a diverse family. Most are marine, but some go from salt water to fresh water to spawn, and a few live only in fresh water. These usually small, silvery fish swim in often immense schools and feed primarily on plankton and small invertebrates. Species may intermingle in these schools, making positive identification difficult at a glance. Like anchovies, herrings are important prey fish for a variety of animals.

Some sharks' best defense may be a good offense, but herrings' best defense is reproduction. Most members of this family spawn seasonally, and spawn with a vengeance. Females disperse up to 200,000 eggs near the surface. After hatching, the larvae may drift with the plankton for several months until they change into juveniles resembling the adults.

There may be as many as 20 marine species in Florida, with two others confined to fresh water. Menhaden support a commercial fishery in the Gulf for processing into fishmeal. Threadfin shad and gizzard shad are both freshwater and brackish species that are important prey for largemouth bass and other large predators. The threadfin shad was introduced into Florida from the Lower Mississippi Valley in the 1930s as a forage fish.

Top: **a school of herrings. The schooling behavior of herrings and anchovies is similar.**

Bottom: **a gizzard shad, a freshwater fish common in Southeast North America.**

VU - PC

Carps, Minnows, Suckers, and Loaches

Carps and Minnows

(Family Cyprinidae)

When is a minnow really a minnow? Any small fish may be called a minnow, but only cyprinids are true minnows. The freshwater Cyprinidae make up one of the largest families of fishes, numbering 2000 or so species. A characteristic of true minnows is that all species lack teeth. Instead, gill arches are modified into structures called "pharyngeal teeth," which they use to chew food in the back of the throat. In addition, minnows and closely related families have their first four vertebrae fused together. Extensions of these vertebrae, called the "Weberian apparatus," touch the air bladder and are thought to help detect sound and other disturbances in the water.

Most minnows are carnivorous, feeding largely on small crustaceans and insects and sometimes on tiny fishes. Several species predominantly eat algae. These include grass carp, an exotic brought to Florida from northeast Asia to help control aquatic weeds. Plant-eaters generally have longer intestines than meat-eaters. This longer gut can sometimes be seen through the belly of certain minnows as a dark, coiled mass.

As a family, minnows occupy a wide range of habitats. Reproductive strategies span a wide range, too. All minnows lay eggs. Some spawn communally, with eggs and milt (fish sperm) distributed indiscriminately. Others spawn in pairs or small groups with elaborate nuptial behavior. Still others build gravel nests. Members of one genus, *Cyprinella*, deposit eggs in crevices. Some minnows lay adhesive eggs and attach them to the undersides of leaves or other floating objects. Natural hybridization among North American minnows is relatively common.

VU - PC

***Top:* a common carp.**

North America is home to about 300 species of cyprinids. Thirty-five species reside in Florida, with 26 known as native, and the others likely introduced. Golden shiners are important forage fish of largemouth bass and are often sold as bait. Flagfin shiners and bluenose shiners are colorful fishes. The redeye chub is found only in springs and spring runs.

BM

***Above:* a bluenose shiner.**

BM

***Above:* a flagfin shiner.**

VU - HWR

***Above:* a blacktail shiner.**

VU - GM

***Above:* fathead minnows. These fish are not native to Florida, but are common bait fish and are often released in Florida waters.**

Suckers

(Family Catostomidae)

Suckers have thick lips and a protrusible mouth (capable of being thrust forward). These features enable these fish to "vacuum," or suck, insect larvae and crustaceans from the bottoms of lakes and streams, thus the name "sucker." Almost all suckers, 69 species, are native to North America. One species occurs in China, and one North American species also occurs in northeastern Siberia.

In North America, the family is found throughout Alaska and much of northern Canada. Suckers range south throughout the US and parts of Mexico to northern Guatemala. In contrast to most other North American fish families, suckers are essentially evenly divided in terms of numbers of species inhabiting eastern and western North America.

Overall, suckers are omnivorous bottom feeders, and the large lips of most species are richly endowed with taste buds. However, three species feed exclusively on mollusks. The pharyngeal teeth of these suckers are short and peg-like, perfectly adapted for crushing shells. As with carps and minnows, suckers possess a Weberian apparatus.

Many suckers inhabit mud-bottomed lakes and rivers where water is often turbid. Because of their abundance and typically large size, suckers account for the greatest portion of biomass in some lakes and streams. Biomass simply means the total mass of living creatures in a given area, such as a lake.

Eight species of Catostomidae live in Florida. Six are confined to the western Panhandle, and of the two occurring farther east (spotted sucker and lake chubsucker), only the latter ranges east and south of the Suwannee River Drainage. Other Florida suckers include the quillback and blacktail redhorse.

VU - GM

VU - GM

Top: **a lake chubsucker.**

Above: **a spotted sucker.**

RED TIDE

In the fall of 1947, early risers in Venice, Florida, woke up to a terrible stench and beaches full of dead fish. The sentiments holding over from World War II may have fueled the claims of nerve gas, but a toxic chemical spill also was blamed. Soon scientists discovered the real culprit, and "red tide" entered the vocabulary of Floridians.

Actually, the red tide phenomenon was nothing new. Reports date back to the 1800s, and red tides occur throughout the world. Of thousands of microscopic algae species in Florida waters, only about a dozen cause harmful algal blooms. Florida's red tides most often result from a species of microscopic marine phytoplankton, a dinoflagellate that produces a potent neurotoxin. The tiny, single celled organism, Gymnodinium breve, *occurs naturally in warm marine waters. Scientists suspect this organism enters a dormant state miles off Florida's west coast, perhaps as cysts that settle to the ocean bed. The warm, strong Gulf Stream currents may carry* G. breve *into the Atlantic and up the East Coast to the Carolinas.*

In Florida, red tides begin 40 to 80 miles offshore in the Gulf. Prevailing ocean currents slowly push the organisms toward the shore, and they reproduce rapidly as they move until red or orange-tinted blooms reach coastal waters. Toxins are produced by millions of cells per gallon of water over many square miles and cause extensive fish kills, contaminate shellfish, and cause respiratory irritation in sensitive people on shore.

During heavy blooms, toxin concentrations kill fish quickly before they can accumulate it in their systems. However, sublethal concentrations can result in fish accumulating the toxin and passing it up the food chain. Evidence suggests such bioaccumulation resulted in the poisoning deaths of 700 dolphins (the mammals) in 1987. Shellfish filter G. breve *from the water and are unaffected by the toxin. However, they can accumulate so much toxin in their tissues that they become toxic to humans. Thus, oysters, clams, mussels, other bivalve mollusks, and whelks found in the vicinity of red tides should not be eaten. Since the toxin becomes airborne in salt spray, it can irritate the skin, eyes, and respiratory systems of sensitive people.*

Red tides are a natural part of Florida's warm marine environment and are unrelated to pollution. In fact, the offending organism plays an important ecological role by converting solar energy to chemical energy through photosynthesis. Why does the red tide organism also generate such trouble? That's still a mystery.

Catfishes

North American Catfishes

(Family Ictaluridae)

Most catfishes are quickly recognized anywhere found. Their best-known features may be their whisker-like barbels (the source of the name, catfish) and the spines at the front of their dorsal and pectoral fins. The spines provide a formidable weapon when erected and locked in place, and many predators find it difficult to swallow a catfish with its fins spread out. To make matters worse, some species have venom glands located at the base of the pectoral spines and can inflict a painful wound. Catfishes use their barbels, which are pressure-sensitive and filled with taste buds, to find food. Catfishes are nocturnal, with poorly developed eyes, making their barbels a very important feature for survival.

VU - JDC

Many people associate catfishes with still, muddy, or even stagnant conditions. Indeed, a few species of bullheads do prefer quiet water. However, the majority of native catfishes prefer clean, well-oxygenated waters with good flow. This is especially true of most of the madtoms. Their preference for such clean conditions makes madtoms particularly vulnerable to habitat degradation and contributes to the scarcity of certain species.

Catfishes are basically carnivorous, though opportunistic feeding habits caused many people to consider them scavengers. Ictalurids spawn in cavities and other protected sites. The male guards the clutch of eggs until they hatch and continues to protect the school of young for a period of time. Perhaps because their spawning habits minimize the potential for cross-fertilization, hybridization among species is rare.

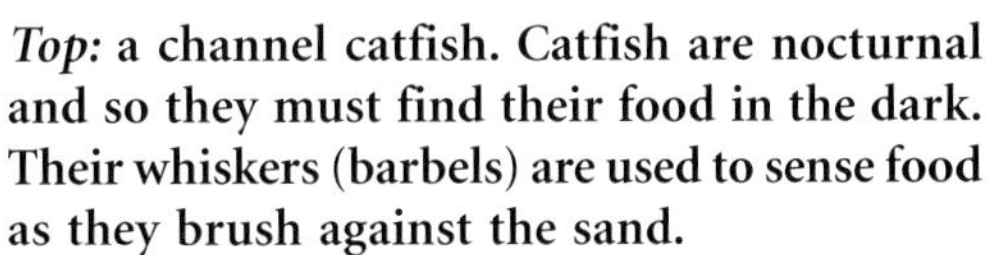

Top: **a channel catfish. Catfish are nocturnal and so they must find their food in the dark. Their whiskers (barbels) are used to sense food as they brush against the sand.**

More than 2200 species of catfishes are known in the world, and there may be many others yet to be discovered. The North American catfishes are the only catfishes native to the US and include 46 species. Several North American catfishes live in Florida, but not all of them are native.

The flathead, or shovelnose catfish was introduced into the western Panhandle and Apalachicola River from the Midwestern US. It is a voracious predator that can severely deplete populations of smaller bullhead catfishes.

The brown catfish, yellow catfish, and spotted catfish often come from sluggish pools and backwaters, though the spotted catfish may prefer faster-flowing conditions. The inappropriately named white catfish of eastern Florida is actually quite dark.

There are three species of madtoms in Florida. Tadpole madtoms and speckled madtoms are found throughout Florida and are often confused with the young of catfishes.

The channel catfish occasionally enters low-salinity coastal waters. It is unique among North American catfishes in that it is grown in fish farms.

VU - HWR

VU - GM

Center: **yellow bullhead.**

Bottom: **tadpole madtom.**

Labyrinth Catfishes
(Walking Catfish)
(Family Clariidae)

Labyrinth catfishes are so named for chambers behind their gills where they store air. In this chamber, spongy organs grow from the upper ends of gill arches, and these and the surrounding skin are rich in blood vessels. This feature makes the walking catfish very efficient at extracting oxygen from water deficient in oxygen, such as stagnant pools. The labyrinth also allows these catfishes to live out of water for long periods of time and makes their overland treks possible. In addition, gills are stiffened and, therefore, don't collapse when the fish leaves water.

No labyrinth catfish is native to North America. They come from Africa, Middle East, and Southeast Asia, where about 100 species are found. In their home regions, walking catfishes are popular food fishes, even raised commercially. However, these fish are highly predatory and some species grow to about two feet in length—a troublesome combination for smaller fishes. One species of walking catfish was introduced inadvertently into Florida in the 1960s. The rest, as they say, is history.

For awhile, the walking catfish was a novelty, almost a celebrity, reported in newspaper accounts and wildlife stories about its habit of "walking" on its stiff pectoral fins through streets and yards from one canal to another in South Florida. Eventually, people realized the truth: walking catfish are here to stay. Cold temperatures may limit their northern expansion, but walking catfish thrive in the southern peninsula.

PC/Seapics.com

PC/Seapics.com

Top: **an albino walking catfish. Albinos were probably imported as a curiosity, but after the species established itself in Florida and time passed, most walking catfish found now are typically dark in color**

Center: **a gafftopsail catfish.**

Bottom: **a hardhead catfish. Both the gafftopsail and the hardhead are commonly caught by fishermen in Florida's coastal waters.**

> **THE HEALING PROPERTIES OF CATFISH SLIME**
>
> *Most folks just want to get it off, if they ever get catfish slime on their hands. However, this gel-like substance secreted by a catfish performs remarkable functions. As with other fishes, the slime reduces friction between the catfish's body and the water and also forms a protective covering over the fish's body which shields it from some infectious agents that are a part of the environment. American catfish secrete this beneficial component of slime just beneath their outer skin. But, catfish slime also contains about 60 proteins important in the healing of wounds in humans. Some of these proteins block bacterial growth. Catfish slime contains coagulants that clot blood and enzymes that stimulate the production of new tissue. Arabs traditionally used the slime of the Arabian catfish to heal cuts and scratches. It was this practice that inspired modern-day scientists to explore the medical benefits of catfish slime.*

Sea Catfishes
(Family Ariidae)

Only two catfish families in the world live primarily in salt water. Florida lays claim to one of these families. Both species of Florida's sea catfishes have the expected "catfish look," having long rays extending from their fins. Both also practice a fascinating method of reproduction: oral incubation. Males carry the fertilized eggs in their mouths until the eggs hatch, and then carry the young until they are fully formed and able to fend for themselves.

Two species occur in Florida, and both are common. The hardhead catfish is sometimes jokingly called the "tourist trout," since tourists catch them frequently — but so do local anglers. Hardheads are truly omnivorous. Their spines are covered with a venomous tissue and can inflict a painful wound. The gafftopsail catfish, or simply sail cat, is easily recognized by the long first rays of its dorsal and pectoral fins.

VU - PC

VU - BB

Pickerels and Mudminnows

Pickerels

(Family Esocidae)

Florida's pickerels are miniature relatives of the famous northern pike and muskellunge. Like their larger cousins, Florida's pickerels are solitary, toothy predators that prey on surface-swimming creatures, including fish, frogs, and an occasional duckling. Voracious feeders, pickerel ambush prey from below or from the cover of aquatic weeds, where their green and brown bodies are readily camouflaged. Usually, they seize the victim's head, then swallow their prey whole. Pickerel, or pike, stake out territories, which they defend against their own kind.

Two species of pickerels are found in Florida. The chain pickerel, or jack, prefers vegetated areas in lakes, ponds, and quiet pools of wider rivers. A three or four pound chain pickerel is considered large. The redfin pickerel grows to about 15 inches and prefers weedy sloughs, backwaters and, sluggish pools of streams. Occasionally redfins are found in the same area with chain pickerel.

Top: **a chain pickerel (subadult).**

Below: **a redfin pickerel.**

VU - HWR

Mudminnows

(Family Umbridae)

Mudminnows are not minnows at all, but are small, hardy fish closely related to pickerels and even look much like them, except with a blunt snout—and, of course, in miniature. They both swim the same, their fins are placed the same, and they hunt in the same way. Mudminnows eat small insects, crustaceans, and fish.

The mudminnows' name stems from both their small size and preferred habitat which is very quiet, weedy waters, usually with a mud bottom. They can breathe atmospheric oxygen, which enables them to survive in poorly-oxygenated water. The eastern mudminnow is the only species in Florida and is restricted to an area from northern Florida south to around Gainesville. It has also been introduced into coastal freshwater systems in northwestern Europe, where it is now common.

Bottom: **a baby eastern mudminnow.**

VU - RJG

Trout-perches and Pirate Perches

Pirate Perches

(Family Aphredoderidae)

The percopsiform fishes are native to North America and include trout-perches and pirate perches.

Florida's pirate perch lives in swamps, vegetated sloughs, and backwaters, usually over a mud bottom. The pirate perch is a nocturnal carnivore, becoming active just prior to dark and reaching peak activity at dawn. Researchers believe these activity peaks correspond to those peaks of the various aquatic invertebrates pirate perch eat. Although pirate perch clearly prefer invertebrates, primarily insects, they readily consume small fishes when invertebrates are scarce.

Top: **a pirate perch.**

Lizardfishes

(Family Synodontidae)

Lizardfishes are relatively small, benthic predators. Benthic organisms typically stay on the bottom, and that is just what lizardfishes do best. They often sit on the sand propped up by their ventral fins, or bury themselves with just their eyes exposed. Their cryptic coloration aids in camouflage, and from such a position, lizardfishes ambush small fishes and shrimps.

Florida may be home to nine species of these aggressive predators including the inshore lizardfish, the most common in Florida. The red lizardfish is found more often on coral reefs. The snakefish has blue and yellow striping on the head and body.

DP/Seapics.com

Above: **a sand diver. This fish is usually found around coral reefs like the red lizardfish, but unlike the inshore lizardfish.**

Bottom, left: **a red lizardfish.**

Bottom, right: **an inshore lizardfish**

BH/Seapics.com

MK/Seapics.com

LEO

Oarfishes

(Family Regalecidae)

Could oarfishes be the sea serpents of old? Their large size and bizarre appearance would match these fish quite well to the tales of ancient mariners. Oarfishes are the largest bony fishes in the world in terms of length, although not in bulk, since they are long and slender. Rarely, they are seen lazing at the surface of the open ocean, but usually they are not seen at all unless an individual dies and washes up on the beach. Usually they live a great depths, up to 2,000 feet or more. There is only one species which is found in many parts of the world.

Members of this order feed in a novel manner. Most fish's jaws are connected to their cheek bones, but not oarfish's. Their mouths are small for their size, but their upper jaw can extend far forward when the oarfish is feeding, enlarging the mouth cavity greatly. This ability may aid oarfish in feeding on small sealife .

The oarfish may be so called because of its oar-like shape or because its style of swimming looks like rowing.

Top: **a huge oarfish which washed ashore at the US Navy SEALs training center on Coronado Island, California.**

Right: **an oarfish found on the beach at Anna Maria Island, Florida.**

DUKE MILLER

Lanternfishes

(Family Myctophidae)

Lanternfishes are distributed in deep temperate and tropical waters virtually around the world. This family of fishes goes largely unnoticed and unknown, but it is the most widely distributed and abundant of deep-water fishes. These small black to silvery-black fish are named for the series of luminescent organs, called photophores, located on their heads and down their bodies. Each photophore is covered by a modified scale that acts like a lens, focusing the light from that photophore.

The arrangement of photophores varies among the species of lanternfish. Scientists believe that these fishes use their luminescent organs to communicate with each other and to attract prey. This luminescence may also serve as camouflage. The glowing undersides may blend with the sun or moonlit water's surface, thus rendering the lanternfish invisible to predators below. The lack of photophores on the backs of many species also enable those species to blend with the darkness of the deep water below, thus masking them from predators above.

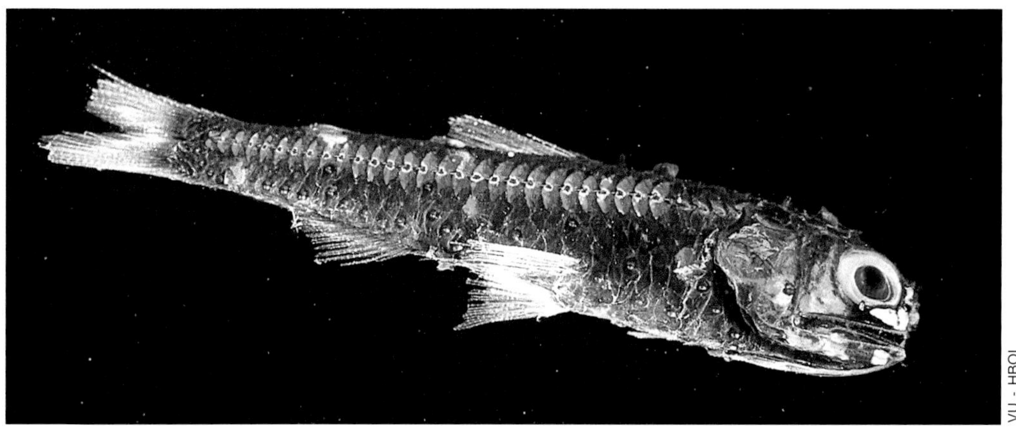

VU - HBOI

Top: **a typical lanternfish.**

Lanternfishes make up a sizable component of the mass of marine animals that reflects sonar and gives the appearance of a false sea bottom above the actual bottom. By day, these fishes live at depths of about 500 feet to around 6,600 feet. At night, they migrate up near the surface to feed on plankton. In turn, lanternfishes become food for tuna, bonito, and other pelagic fishes. This daily migration distributes life-giving energy in the deep ocean by bringing it from the surface to the depths. There are approximately 235 species of lanternfishes worldwide, and identification is often relatively easy since it is based largely on the arrangement of photophores.

Many species in this large family are found in Florida's waters. The metallic lanternfish occurs primarily off the East Coast. Like most lanternfishes, it performs a vertical migration at night and can be caught in dip nets around lights.

Cusk-eels, Pearlfish, and Brotulas

Pearlfishes

(Family Carapidae)

Pearlfishes comprise about 30 species worldwide. Some pearlfishes are free-living, but most are "inquilines," residing within bodies of other animals. Usually sea cucumbers have the dubious distinction of playing host to pearlfishes, but sea stars or oysters are used by some species. Those pearlfishes that live in sea cucumbers often eat the gonads of their host. It appears that larval pearlfishes can delay transformation, within limits, until they find a suitable host.

Pearlfishes are found in all oceans but are rarely seen because they spend most of their lives hiding in their host, only venturing out at night to feed. Two species are native to Florida, including the pearlfish.

DP/Seapics.com

Top: **this species of pearlfish lives in sea cucumbers.**

FLORIDA'S AQUATIC HABITATS

Florida's 1,700 rivers and 1,300 miles of coastline span from temperate waters to the northern edge of the tropics. Florida isn't all sand and surf. A great diversity of aquatic habitats supports a great wealth of fish species.

Creeks

Most of Florida's creeks are permanent, rather than seasonal streams, and the flow of water is slow compared to northern streams. Florida, after all, is rather flat.

Rivers

Florida's rivers vary greatly. In southeastern Florida, most waterways today are box-cut channels. Yet Florida contains several slow-flowing, relatively deep rivers, such as the St. Johns. On the other hand, the Withlacoochee River in North Florida is whitewater in nature.

Springs

Most large springs in Florida are artesian. The water rises through deep, vertical limestone holes. Spring water is crystal clear, cool, and alkaline. Because of the large quantity of phosphates in spring water, springs and spring runs are among the most productive aquatic habitats.

Ditches

Ditches are a common sight throughout Florida. Where permanent water exists, ditches may be rich in aquatic life.

Ponds

Ponds in Florida vary greatly, but nearly all lack surface streams draining in or out. Sinkhole ponds form by the dissolution of underlying limestone as rainwater percolates downward to the water table. Alligator ponds are created as alligators clear away soil to make small, open-water areas. Except during extreme droughts, alligator ponds retain water year-round, providing a refuge for aquatic life during dry seasons.

Lakes

Many lakes in Florida form by the dissolution of underlying limestone. A few, such as Lake Okeechobee, seem to occupy natural depressions in the land's surface, which may have been hollows in the ancient sea floor. The disappearing lakes in northern Florida go dry during extensive droughts.

Marshes

Marshes are common in peninsular Florida. Marshes are wetlands which lack trees. Many marshes were once lakes. The transition from lake to marsh still occurs due to eutrophication. As decaying vegetation fills the basin, great deposits of peat form and eventually replace the water. The Central Everglades is a vast basin marsh seasonally inundated with a thin sheet of water that flows slowly to the south.

Swamps

Swamps are wetlands containing trees, such as those dominated by cypress.

Tidal Rivers

The lower reaches of all Florida's rivers that flow to the Atlantic or Gulf are influenced by tides. In these reaches, fresh water mixes with salt water to create estuaries rich in aquatic life.

Salt Marshes

Herbaceous salt marshes are found throughout coastal Florida. Estuaries north of Charlotte Harbor on the Gulf coast and Indian River Lagoon on the Atlantic contain the greatest acreage of salt marsh. Aquatic life in these marshes must be able to tolerate a wide range of environmental conditions.

Mangroves

Mangroves are found in Central and South Florida. They are similar looking trees that are either salt tolerant or process salt. They form coastal estuaries rich in fish life.

Sea Grass Meadows

Extensive sea grass communities exist in the shallow waters of almost all of Florida's estuaries, as well as in portions of the northeastern Gulf. Sea grass meadows make up the richest fish communities in Florida's estuaries.

Reefs

Exposed bedrock offers habitats for many fish and invertebrates throughout Florida's coasts. Most of this bedrock is limestone that has eroded into undercut ledges and holes and may form the only vertical structure on an otherwise featureless bottom.

Florida is fortunate to possess a true coral reef that is most extensive from Virginia Key to the Dry Tortugas. Other shallow reefs with corals extend as far north as St. Lucie Inlet and the eastern Gulf.

MK/Seapics.com

Toadfishes

(Family Batrachoididae)

"Beautiful" would never describe Florida's toadfishes. Even "homely" is generous. However, there are toadfish in other parts of the world that are quite beautiful.

Toadfishes live on the bottom in shallow coastal waters and estuaries. They are rugged fish with strong jaws and stout, blunt teeth suited to crushing small fishes and crustaceans. In keeping with their lethargic lifestyle, toadfishes seek out sheltering crevices in oyster bars, as well as old tires, cans, and other rubble. In such places, they also lay eggs.

For such an otherwise shy fish, toadfishes are noisy. Special muscles vibrate the swim bladder, producing grunts and croaks that sometimes can be heard through the hull of a boat. Males even attract prospective mates to their holes by calling to them.

Top: **an oyster toadfish.**

GREAT DADS

Real homebodies, male toadfishes often call to their mates. Once she is inside the nest, the female releases her eggs, which attach to the sides of the nest by means of a sticky disk. The male then fertilizes them. More than one female may use the same nest, but once they leave, they don't return. The males are left to guard the eggs alone, and perform a superb job. They never leave the nest while brooding eggs. Presumably, they eat what they can ambush at the entrance to their holes, but they become noticeably thinner during this period. After the eggs hatch, the males continue to provide care until the young leave the nest. During this time, the free-swimming young may sit on their dad's head or crowd under his body.

Four species of toadfish live in Florida waters. The gulf toadfish is caught frequently by anglers fishing from bridges and jetties along Florida's Gulf Coast. Oyster toadfish replace gulf toadfish along the Atlantic coast north of Cape Sable. The unusual Atlantic midshipman got its name from the bioluminescent photophores on its belly and sides, resembling the buttons on a 19th Century naval midshipman's uniform. Photophores are light emitting organs or spots on certain fishes. The midshipman also has a venomous spine on its gill cover, but the venom has no serious effects on organisms as large as humans.

Anglerfishes

Goosefishes

(Monkfish or Anglerfish)

(Family Lophiidae)

Goosefishes, more commonly known as anglerfishes, are so named because of their prehensile "fishing rod," actually the front dorsal spine, which is attached to the tip of the snout. At the tip of this fishing rod, or illicium, hangs the "lure" which the fish can wriggle like a worm to attract a potential meal.

Goosefishes have mastered the art of camouflage. With its dark, mottled skin, a goosefish practically disappears as it lies flattened against the sea floor. Other bottom-dwelling fishes are attracted by the wriggling lure, and with lightning speed the goosefish inhales its meal into its huge mouth.

Three species of goosefish find a home in Florida. All of them are brown bottom-dwellers that live at depths too deep for divers and snorklers to observe ordinarily. However, fishing trawls regularly bring up goosefishes from the depths and sell them as "monkfish." For centuries, goosefishes were the only anglerfishes known anywhere. Today, numerous species are recognized around the world.

FG/Seapics.com

The goosefish reaches the southern limit of its range in northeastern Florida. The blackfin goosefish is more common to the south.

Bottom: **a goosefish.**

MK/Seapics.com

Top, and middle: **polka-dot batfishes.**

IV - MPO

Batfishes

(Family Ogcocephalidae)

If "grotesque" describes many of the frogfishes, "bizarre" would fit the batfishes. The head and trunk are broad and flattened, often triangular, with a projecting snout, or rostrum. The illicium, or fishing rod, is shorter than in other anglerfishes, and retracts into a groove beneath the rostrum when the batfish is not actively fishing for food. Batfishes ambush their food, and in addition to small fishes, they also eat snails, clams, and worms. Like the other anglerfishes, batfishes depend on stealth and camouflage to ambush prey and hide from predators. Most batfishes are bottom-dwellers in deep water, where they walk along the bottom on peculiar pectoral fins, which resemble hands extending from arm-like stalks.

Florida waters are home to ten batfish species. Most can be difficult to identify. The polkadot batfish is one of the few batfishes living in shallow water. Other species include the shortnose, roughback, and pancake batfish, which displays striking pigment patterns and is sometimes seen around coral reefs.

JJ/Seapics.com

Bottom, left and right: **shortnose batfishes.**

JJ/Seapics.com

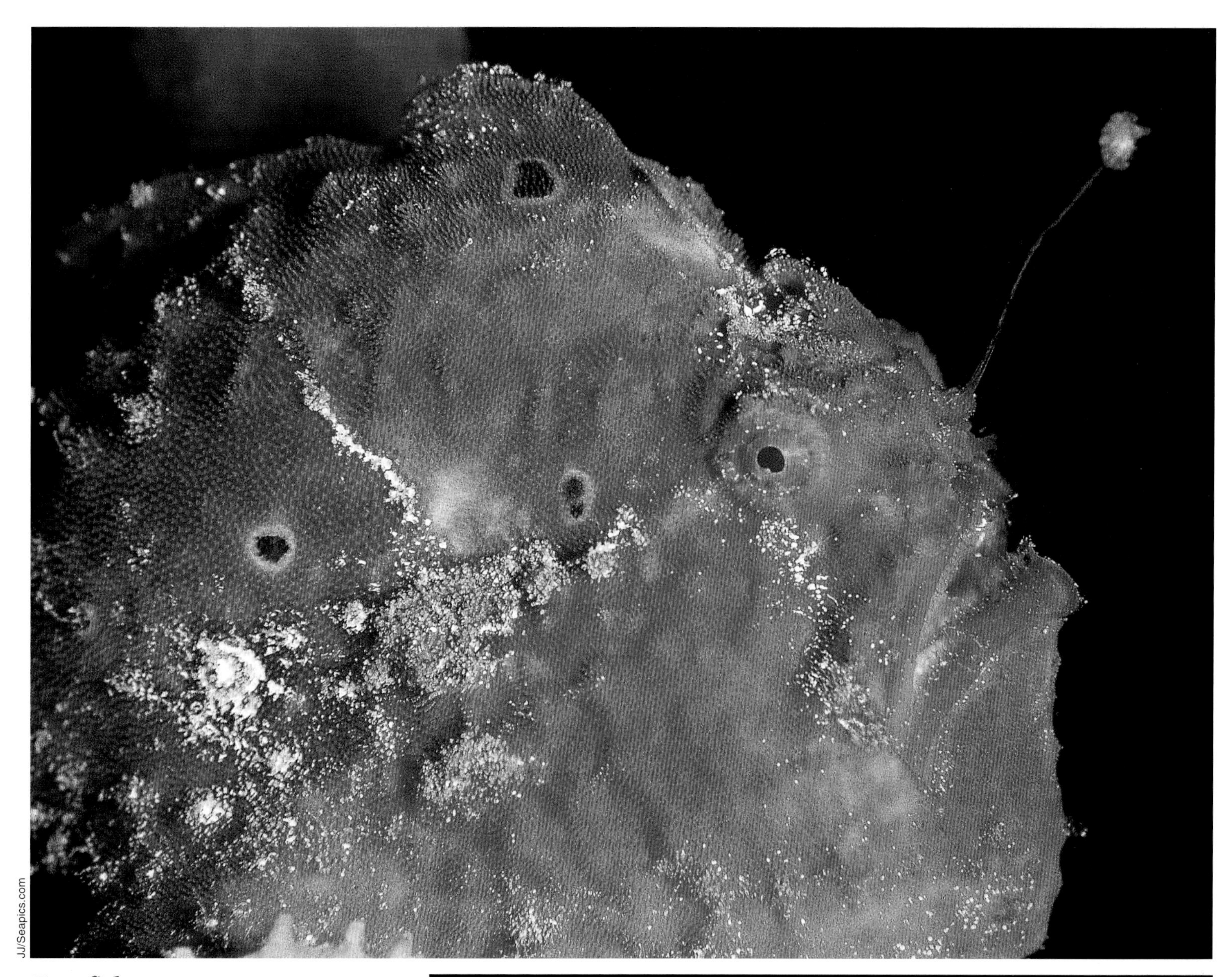

JJ/Seapics.com

Frogfishes

(Family Antennariidae)

The frogfishes are the most brightly colored and likely seen family of anglerfishes, in part because some live on coral reefs. In contrast to goosefishes, frogfishes have a high, slightly compressed head and body. Like goosefishes, frogfishes possess a fishing rod and lure and are masters of camouflage, in spite of their bright colors. Warty skin and fleshy appendages help them to blend into the background. They also can change color to match surroundings, making them practically invisible to both prey and predator.

Frogfishes are slow swimmers and rather sedentary, but they can "walk" if they feel the urge to move around. They use two gaits. In one, they alternately move paired fins in a step much like that of four-legged animals. In the other, they use their pectoral fins like crutches, making short hops.

Six species of frogfishes inhabit Florida's waters. The longlure frogfish may be the most common. Other species include ocellated frogfish, Florida's largest frogfish; dwarf frogfish, maturing at just over an inch; and striated frogfish, formerly known as the split-lure frogfish. The sargassumfish inhabits floating sargassum weed, where it walks among the branches using its pectoral fins.

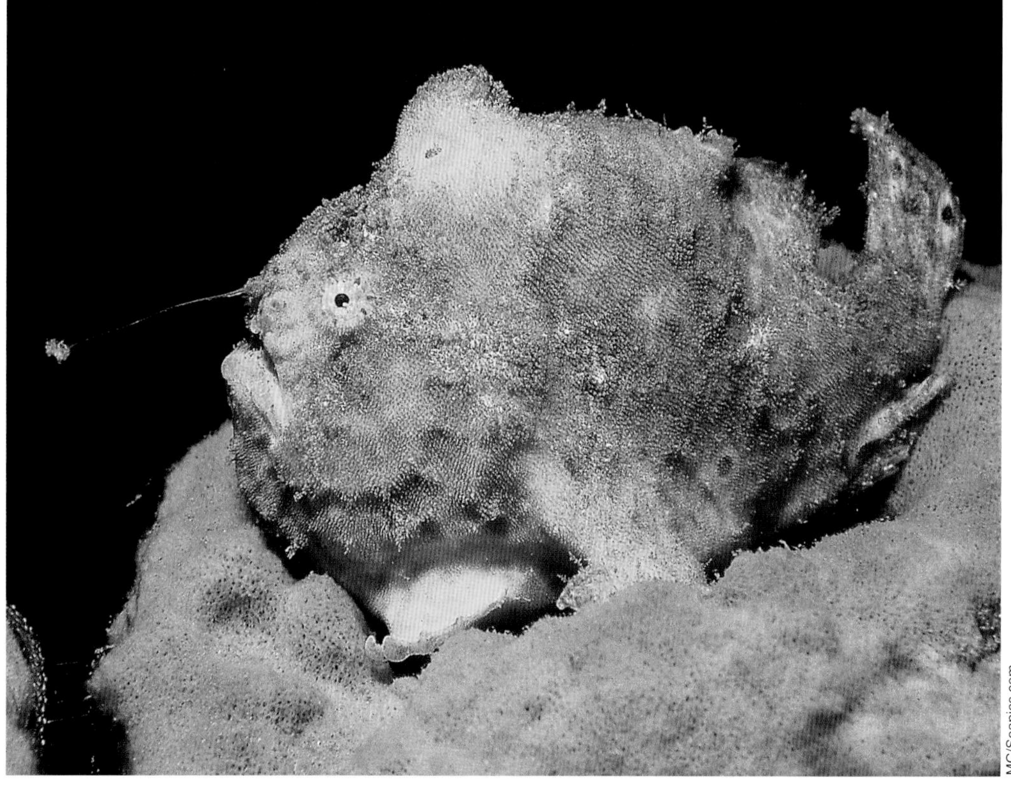

MC/Seapics.com

Top and above: **longlure frogfishes with lures extended. The frogfish above is on a yellow sponge.**

MK/Seapics.com

SG

DDM/Seapics.com

MC/Seapics.com

Top, left: **a striated frogfish.**

Top, right: **an oscellated frogfish.**

Middle and bottom: **sargassumfishes. These fish differ from other frogfish in that they spend their entire lives in floating sargassumweed rather than on the bottom.**

DP/Seapics.com

ANGLING FISH

Fishes that fish? For these squat, sedentary fishes, angling seems quite appropriate. They would stay pretty hungry if they had to chase down food. Their angling appears to be deliberate. They spot intended prey and direct their lure toward the unsuspecting morsel. When the hungry little victim swims up close to investigate the wiggling "worm," the angling fish engulfs its meal in a move too fast to follow with the naked eye. In a flash, the would-be predator becomes the prey.

DP/Seapics.com

Mullets

(Order Mugiliformes)

Mullets

(Family Mugilidae)

Mullets are primarily a marine family, though some enter fresh water and may even live there for extended periods. A distinctive feature of this family is its adipose eyelid. These fleshy, transparent extensions of the rims of the eye sockets cover most of the eye, leaving an oval area at the center exposed. Mullets feed primarily on algae and detritus, which they scrape from the surface of hard objects, such as submerged tree roots, with their small triangular mouths. Mullets have muscular stomachs and long intestines to handle a largely vegetarian diet. All mullets are strong swimmers that school near the surface.

Six species occur in Florida. Mountain mullet, sometimes called freshwater mullet, occur sporadically around the state and can be distinguished from other mullets by their yellowish skin and lack of an adipose eyelid. The white mullet enters fresh water occasionally and lacks dark stripes on its sides.

The striped, or black, mullet enjoys a worldwide distribution, a trait rare among inshore fishes. This species regularly enters fresh water, ranging far upstream in all of Florida's major rivers. It is also found in Lake Okeechobee. Yet the striped mullet remains a true marine species, drifting with pelagic plankton during its larval stage and seldom venturing beyond the estuaries as juveniles. Adults, though, can be real gadabouts.

VU - KL

Top: **white mullet.**
Bottom: **white mullet.**
Opposite page, top: **striped mullet.**

WHY DO MULLET JUMP?

Whether fishing in open waters of Lake Okeechobee, or poling through seagrass beds in Sarasota Bay, chances are great that even a casual observer will see several mullet jump near the boat—or maybe into it. Why? Some fish leap from the water to capture flying insects, but mullet feed primarily on non-flying algae. Biologists theorize that mullet, and certain other fishes, often jump to escape predators. Apparently, a jumping fish may leave a predator's field of vision when the jumper leaves the water. Of course, jumping mullet don't go far and may still get eaten by an alert snook or bottlenose dolphin. Sometimes, too, mullet are found in water that's both hot and low in oxygen, conditions not favorable for most predatory fishes.

Mullet are also known to jump when they come up to a shallow bar or shoal. Sometimes, too, as a school rolls along, one will jump, then two or three more will follow before quickly rejoining the school. Other theories about jumping mullet suggest they are cleaning their gill rakers or ridding their bodies of parasites. Sound farfetched?

So, then, why do mullet jump? Maybe a wise old Cracker figured it out: "Mullet jump 'cause they happy."

DP/Seapics.com

WHY MULLET ARE FREQUENTLY SEEN SCHOOLING AT THE SURFACE, GULPING AIR

Often, groups of mullet can be seen in canals and shallow bays just milling about near the water's surface. The somewhat flattened head of a mullet and its upward-turned mouth enable mullet to utilize the thin, oxygen-rich layer of water at the surface (the air/water interface). Thus mullet can survive quite well in the warm, oxygen-poor conditions encountered in many areas of Florida's estuaries in the summer. Mullet may seem to be gulping air, but actually they are drawing through their gills the thin surface layer of water that is highly oxygenated. They also may be feeding on algae at the water's surface.

CCL

MULLET IN COURT---THE FAMOUS "FISH OR FOWL" CASE

In 1919, several youths were arrested for fishing out of season. They hired colorful Tampa attorney, Pat Whitacre, Sr., to represent them. They had been caught red-handed and couldn't deny catching the mullet in question. But the crafty lawyer decided they could deny they had caught fish because mullet have gizzards, and only birds have gizzards. As proof, he offered texts showing that fish don't have gizzards.

As reported by the Tampa Tribune, Whitaker recalled, "I conceded that mullet lived in water like fish, but that didn't make them fish. Whales live in the water, but they aren't fish. Beavers live in the water, but they are not fish. The only thing I could think of was that these mullet were some kind of aquatic fowl." The judge dismissed the case. This case inspired the Florida legistlature to rewrite its fish conservation law to specifically mention mullet. According to legend, it might have helped that the defendants were related to the judge.

In reality, a mullet's "gizzard" is a muscular portion of the mullet's stomach. A bird's gizzard is a separate organ that repeatedly contracts when the bird eats, thus crushing the seeds and other hard items the bird consumes. The bird also consumes sand or small pebbles, and this grit collects in the bird's gizzard where it aids that organ in its work.

Though not a true gizzard, the muscular (pyloric) portion of a mullet's stomach functions in much the same way. Mullet consume a largely vegetarian diet. The mullet also consumes sediment while feeding. The gritty paricles enter the pyloric portion of the stomach and form a paste that helps grind the plant material, thus crushing the tough cell walls and releasing the nutrients to be digested.

VU - GM

Silversides

SILVERSIDES INTRODUCTION

Most silversides are marine species, but the order also includes brackish and freshwater species. "Silversides" accurately describes these fish since one of their distinctive features is a silvery horizontal stripe running the length of the body. Silversides take a peculiar interest in floating objects, often butting into or jumping over twigs, or other debris.

Silversides like open water, where they usually travel in schools near the surface where they feed on plankton.

In turn, they serve as important forage for a great number of larger predatory fishes.

There are about 160 silverside species divided between two families. Most members of both families lay eggs in algae mats, or other vegetation, and the eggs typically have projecting threads and may even sit at the end of a stalk.

Silversides
(Family Atherinopsidae)

The great majority of Western Hemisphere (New World) silversides (50 species or so) are placed in this family. The tidewater silverside is found in high salinity waters. The brook silverside lives only in fresh water and is endemic to the southeastern US. The inland silverside is a shoreline fish, preferring low salinity, and even enters rivers.

Top: **brook silversides.**

Silversides
(Family Atherinidae)

Only two New World silversides are now classified within this family. The hardhead silverside often is found in shallows and reefs of southern Florida. The reef silverside prefers more offshore waters and reefs. Large schools of this species delight divers by opening a gap in their school to allow the divers to pass through and coming together again behind the divers immediately afterwards.

VU - DSA

Above: **a rough silverside.**

VU - LD

Above: **a tidewater silverside.**

Flyingfishes, Needlefishes, and Halfbeaks

Needlefishes

(Family Belonidae)

Almost every visitor to Florida's beaches or bays has seen a needlefish, and many an inshore angler has sworn at these chronic bait stealers. These surface-dwelling predators can be recognized easily by their long jaws full of small, needle-like teeth. Needlefishes, though sometimes called saltwater gars, are very slender and more closely related to flying fishes and halfbeaks. In fact, needlefishes go through a "halfbeak" stage in development, when the lower jaw is extended beyond the upper jaw. During this stage needlefishes eat plankton. The "nose" transforms from the halfbeak to the needlenose as the needlefish converts from eating plankton to eating fish.

Seven species of needelefish, mostly marine, stalk prey in Florida's waters. The flat needlefish is an uncommon offshore needlefish sometimes seen in large concentrations around schools of spawning red drum. The keeltail needlefish is an offshore tropical species. Houndfish are large needlefish that usually stay well offshore but occasionally venture inshore. The Atlantic needlefish is most likely to be seen by beachgoers and bay anglers. This common inshore species occasionally swims far upstream into fresh water. Tiny Atlantic needlefish, as well as adults, have been seen in the Ichetucknee River in North Florida, suggesting this species may spawn there.

DP/Seapics.com

Top: a school of needlefish swimming just below the surface.

Left: a redfin needlefish.

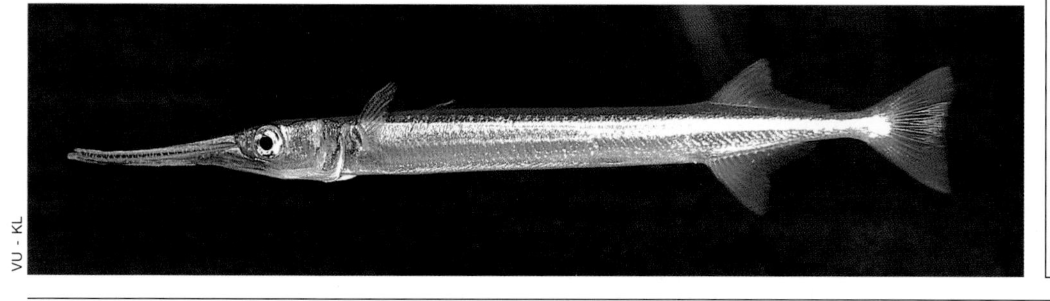

VU - KL

NEEDLEFISH STORIES

When Floridians think about needlefish at all, it is usually with derision because they are not good to eat and they steal bait. But, needlefish behavior can be captivating. Needlefish frequently skip along the surface, and larger needlefish are great leapers, sometimes making spectacular jumps. With their long, thin, and bony snouts, jumping needlefish have impaled people who were wading or in small boats, especially at night near lights. One unfortunate fisherman died when a leaping houndfish jumped toward a light in his canoe and impaled him.

Halfbeaks

(Family Hemiramphidae)

Like flyingfishes and needlefishes, halfbeaks dwell at the surface. Most species of halfbeaks have long lower jaws that extend well past their very short upper jaws. Equally as noteworthy as their namesake jaws, the lower lobe of the halfbeaks' caudal (tail) fin is usually longer than the upper lobe. This disparity enables halfbeaks to skip along the surface, but halfbeaks can't "fly" like flyingfishes because they lack the greatly enlarged pectoral fins of flyingfishes. Two genera of offshore halfbeaks do have pectorals just long enough to stay airborne a little longer than normal for halfbeaks. These genera have been dubbed "flying halfbeaks" for this reason. Halfbeaks are primarily herbivores, eating sea grasses and algae, but a few species eat small fishes and invertebrates.

At least four species of halfbeaks occur regularly in Florida. The ballyhoo is the most common halfbeak around coral reefs. Other species include the balao, silverstripe halfbeak, and week halfbeak.

DP/Seapics.com

Above: ballyhoo are more likely to be found around coral reefs than any other halfbeak. The name is probably a corruption of the Spanish word for halfbeaks which is _bala_.

DW/Seapics.com

TP/Seapics.com

DP/Seapics.com

Top, left: **a California flyingfish taking off.**

Top, right: **a California flyingfish in flight.**

Left: **a bluntnose flyingfish (a Florida species).**

Flyingfishes

(Family Exocoetidae)

Famous the world over, flyingfishes can spread their large pectoral fins and glide above the surface, sometimes for surprisingly long distances. Flyingfishes occupy surface waters in tropical and sub-tropical oceans, usually over deep water.

Ecologists recognize two broad groups within this family. The offshore group lives over 200 miles from shore. The inshore group lives less than 200 miles from shore and enters bays. In general, though, few flyingfishes come very close to shore.

Two other groupings are also used in referring to flyingfishes. Four-winged flyingfishes possess large pelvic fins, as well as large pectoral fins. Two-winged flyingfishes have small pelvic fins and large pectoral fins. Just so matters don't get too simple, three species don't have wing-like pectorals at all.

The largest flyingfish is a Pacific Ocean species that grows to 20 inches and may weigh over two pounds. The smallest flyingfish reaches just over five inches and weighs about an ounce. Regardless of their size, flyingfishes appear to live no longer than a year or two, probably dying after their first spawning season.

Eleven species of flyingfishes are recognized in Florida, including the fourwing flyingfish, which lives up to its name and is found in the Atlantic and Gulf. The spotfin flyingfish also has four "wings."

MASTERS OF FLIGHT?

Flyingfishes have fascinated people for many years because of their apparent bird-like ability to fly. They don't really fly, however; they glide. It can be a long glide, for sure, but glide it remains. Just how well they glide depends on the size of their pectoral fins, their "wings." In two-winged flying fishes, only the pectoral fins are enlarged. These species (genus Exocoetus*) stay just under the surface while they build up speed. When they have reached the correct speed, they extend their pectoral fins and launch into the air. Two-winged species may glide as far as 80 feet before splash-down.*

Four-winged flyingfishes do even better. These members of the subfamily Cypselurinae have both pectoral and pelvic fins enlarged, although the pectorals are still much larger than the pelvic fins. These species taxi much like aircraft. Once they break through the surface, they continue building up speed by keeping the lower lobe of their tail fin in the water and rapidly sweeping their tail side-to-side. In this way, these remarkable fishes can reach speeds up to 37 miles per hour and zip along as much as 650 feet in a flight that may last 30 seconds. Not exactly flight? True, but to a pursuing barracuda, it probably did seem like these fish just flew away.

Pupfishes, Rivulines, Topminnows, Killifishes, and Livebearers

Rivulines

(Family Aplocheilidae)

If "hardy" could be packaged and sold, it would likely come in the form of a rivuline. The tropical rivulines typically live in heavily vegetated, shallow marshes and pools. They feed primarily on aquatic invertebrates, including mosquito larvae. Rivulines tolerate a high degree of salinity. Some, in fact, inhabit areas of environmental extremes lethal to most other fishes.

Florida's single species of rivuline, the mangrove rivulus is just such a "tough cookie." As its common name suggests, this fish lives in the shallow, mud-bottomed ditches and mangroves. It is well-known for occupying crab burrows. In these burrows, space is restricted, water temperature and hydrogen sulfide levels high, and dissolved oxygen is low. This little mud-colored fish survives it all. It even has the ability to live in a kind of dormant state (aestivate) for at least 30 days in moist mud.

Aestivation isn't the only odd survival trick of this little rivulus. Individuals in Florida's population of *R. marmoratus* function as internally self-fertilizing hermaphrodites. In other words, a single fish produces both sperm and eggs and fertilizes itself internally. The result: a virtual replica. This trait represents the ultimate in inbreeding and produces a genetic sameness that has made the mangrove rivulus an important subject for research.

Top: **a mangrove rivulus**

Outwardly, all *R. marmoratus* look like females. Indeed, males are very rare in Florida. In other parts of its range in the Caribbean and Central America, however, females produce eggs, and males fertilize them, as normally expected.

Pupfishes

(Family Cyprinodontidae)

The small, deep-bodied pupfishes can survive extreme environmental conditions. It's a good thing, too, because they tend to live in habitats that test their mettle.

Florida lays claim to three attractive and abundant pupfishes which range from marine to fresh water. The sheepshead minnow typically lives in salt marshes throughout Florida in extremes of heat, salinity, and low oxygen avoided by other fishes. An isolated population, now considered a separate subspecies, is restricted to several freshwater lakes in the upper St. Johns River.

The beautiful flagfish is endemic to peninsular Florida. It inhabits heavily vegetated sloughs, other sluggish waters, and sometimes enters brackish water areas.

VU - JM

Above: **sheephead minnows. These fish are not actually minnows, from a strictly scientific view.**

VU - DSA

Left: **a flagfish. The flagfish is actually a freshwater fish, although it is salt-tolerant.**

Topminnows and Killifishes

(Family Fundulidae)

This family includes 40 or so species found in fresh, brackish, and saltwater habitats of North and Central America, Bermuda, and Cuba. Accurately named, topminnows spend most of their time at or near the surface. All over Florida people see members of this family in ponds and ditches, under bridges, and just about everywhere else that water collects for short periods.

Topminnows and killifishes feed largely on insects and other aquatic invertebrates. Being rather opportunistic, they also eat plant material and may even scavenge dead animal matter. Many species also display a high degree of salt tolerance. Though few species regularly inhabit a marine environment, many can adapt to salinity levels of about two-thirds sea water. Most of these same species are unusually tolerant of hot and cold temperatures.

These fishes are egg layers. Spawning usually occurs in aquatic vegetation, where eggs attach to the plants by strands of mucous. At least two Florida species, the marsh and bayou killifish, live in habitats that may become dry during certain seasons. Their eggs remain viable in the dry substrate for an extended period, hatching when water returns.

Other common Florida species include the golden topminnow, lined topminnow, pygmy killifish, and bluefin killifish. The longnose killifish and gulf killifish are species which are completely marine.

BM

BM

Top: **banded topminnows.**

Right: **a blackspotted topminnow.**

SG

Above: **a golden topminnow.**

VU - RJG

Above: **a golden topminnow (female).**

VU - RGA

Above: **a lined topminnow (male).**

BM

Above: **a lined topminnow (female).**

Livebearers

(Family Poeciliidae)

Perhaps the livebearers are the best-known family of fishes because of the widespread popularity of the guppy in home aquariums. The guppy makes up only one species of livebearer, however. There may be close to 290 species worldwide.

Poeciliidae is a family of New World fishes, ranging across both American continents. The family is most often thought of as a freshwater family, but most species display a high degree of salt tolerance. A high proportion of the species in this family occur in Central America, and it is theorized livebearers originated there.

Poeciliids are among the smallest of fishes. Indeed, this family includes the smallest freshwater fish native to North America, the least killifish. This diminutive livebearer tops out at just over an inch for the female and considerably less for the male. Though least killifish are abundant throughout Florida, few people ever see them due to their shy nature and preference for heavily vegetated waters.

The poeciliids are viviparous, as the family's common name suggests. To be completely accurate, though, the South American genus, *Tomeurus,* is actually an egg-layer. That oddball aside, males introduce sperm packets, or spermatophores, into the female by means of a specialized anal fin, in which the third, fourth, and fifth rays are modified into a peculiar organ known as the gonopodium. The structure of the gonopodium is so specific to species that, in some cases, accurate identification can be made only by using males. The fertilized female can store sperm up to ten months, resulting in successive broods being fertilized from a single mating. Thus, broods in various stages of development may be simultaneously present, a condition known as superfetation.

The livebearers possess a fortunate feature of the family. Upward oriented mouths permit poeciliids to utilize the thin film of oxygenated surface water during periods of low oxygenation. The orientation of the mouths also indicates feeding habits. Most species of livebearers eat small aquatic insects and very small fishes found at or near the water's surface. Others are truly omnivorous, and some feed primarily on plant matter. Some species are noted for their cannibalistic tendencies toward their own young.

Four species of livebearers are native to Florida. A greater number of non-native species have become naturalized in parts of the state as a result of accidental releases. One native of South Florida's coast, the mangrove gambusia lives almost entirely in salt water. Another common native, the sailfin molly has both freshwater and brackish water populations. The western and eastern mosquitofishes have been introduced around the world as a mosquito control agent. Mosquitofishes do eat mosquito larvae. They also are very aggressive and eat the young of other fishes. Many introductions of mosquitofishes have had detrimental effects on certain native fish populations.

Livebearers introduced and established in Florida include the predaceous pike killifish, variable platyfish, green swordtail, and guppy.

GS

Top: **a sailfin molly.**

Below: **a least killifish.**

Second below: **a gulf killifish.**

Bottom: **a pike killifish.**

VU - RJG

WNR

VU - PC

Squirrelfishes

(Family Holocentridae)

All members of the Beryciformes are marine fishes. Some species prefer shallow water, but most live in deep water where they avoid sunlight, either remaining deep, or staying within the shelter of caves or similar structure during the day, and feeding at night.

Squirrelfishes and soldierfishes comprise the largest family in the order, with some 75 species worldwide. These fishes typically display a reddish color and have large eyes, strong fin spines, and a forked tail. Most members of this family live in shallow water around reefs and areas of rocky bottom, although a few species live at depths over 600 feet.

In many squirrelfishes, the swim bladder is connected to the skull in such a way it amplifies sound. Sound often is used in courtship behavior of these fishes. They are egg layers, and the larvae go through an extended pelagic existence, often found out at sea.

Most of Florida's eleven species of squirrelfishes are nocturnal reef dwellers and are usually bright red or orange. They feed primarily on small fishes and invertebrates. Common species include the squirrelfish, which sometimes descends to depths of 600 feet. The longspine squirrelfish is a little fish frequently seen by divers. The longjaw squirrelfish is more active during the day than most squirrelfish and is sometimes placed in the genus *Flammeo.*

BH/Seapics.com

Top: **blackbar soldierfishes.**

Bottom: **a longspine squirrelfish.**

DP/Seapics.com

Pipefishes, Seahorses, Trumpetfishes, and Cornetfishes

Pipefishes and Seahorses

(Family Syngnathidae)

Seahorses are the stuff of storybooks. Myths and folklore grew out of the peculiar shape and habits of these small, slender fishes once described as half fish and half horse. Legends aside, the pipefishes and seahorses make up one of the most fascinating families of marine fishes. They are found in almost every sea and ocean.

The males in this family incubate eggs produced by the female. The brood pouch of male seahorses is enclosed in the abdomen, whereas in pipefishes, this pouch may be located on the abdomen or tail. The location and size of the pouch aids in identifying species within this family.

As many as 21 species of pipefishes and seahorses live in Florida. Most species live in salt or brackish water, but the Gulf pipefish enters freshwater portions of the St. Johns and Suwannee rivers and likely breeds there. The Gulf pipefish living in the Santa Fe River, a tributary of the Suwannee, probably never leave fresh water.

An especially curious member of this family, the pipehorse, looks like a pipefish but with the grasping (prehensile) tail of a seahorse. It is apparently a rare resident of the Gulf, including South Florida.

Other Florida species include the whitenose pipefish of higher salinity waters; sargassum pipefish usually found in floating clumps of sargassum weed; and the lined seahorse.

***Right:** a* **longsnout seahorse.**

Below: **a shortfin pipefish next to a starfish.**

DP/Seapics.com

MK/Seapics.com

THE DIFFERENCE BETWEEN SEAHORSES AND PIPEFISHES

All pipefishes and seahorses have tiny, tubular snouts, bodies encased in bony armor, and pectoral, but no pelvic fins. The two groups differ in that pipefishes have the head oriented in a continuous line with the axis of the stiff, slender body. The head of seahorses is bent at a right angle to the body. Seahorses also possess a prehensile tail they wrap around sea-grasses and other objects to hold themselves in place. Seahorses are poor swimmers but can swim slowly by undulating their dorsal fin. Seahorses and pipefishes feed primarily on minute invertebrates they suck into their tiny mouths.

DP/Seapics.com

TOO POPULAR FOR THEIR OWN GOOD?

Seahorses must contend with a lot of risks simply to grow up. Out of the thousands of young a pair of seahorses may produce in their lives, very few live long enough to mate even once. Storms tear seahorses from their anchors and cast them adrift or, even worse, onto shore. Crabs, skates, rays, and other fishes love to eat seahorses.

Humans are drawn to seahorses for a variety of reasons. Seahorses have been used for their supposed medicinal value by Chinese and other Asian cultures for centuries. To some Asians, the seahorse is a wonder drug which can cure baldness, impotency and asthma, enhance virility, lower cholesterol, and prevent arteriosclerosis (hardening of the arteries). Other than tradition, however, no medical evidence supports these health claims.

Seahorses also are captured for the aquarium trade. The special charm of these little fishes endear them to many saltwater aquarium hobbyists. However, seahorses are notoriously difficult to keep in an aquarium. They require tiny live food offered frequently and very clean water. Succeeding with seahorses in an aquarium requires more time and effort, than most hobbyists can devote.

Almost everyone has time for souvenirs, though. Judging by the number of dried seahorses made into key chains and jewelry or just sold as trinkets, seahorses sadly make great souvenirs.

No one knows how many seahorses there are. What is known is that seahorses live in some of the most vulnerable coastal environments: sea-grass beds, mangroves, and coral reefs. Their habitat needs and their popularity make seahorse conservation a difficult task.

Top and bottom: **lined seahorse.**

MK/Seapics.com

MR. MOM

Aristotle thought a seahorse broke apart during the spawning season. What he likely observed was the seahorse giving birth—the male seahorse, that is.

Rare among fishes, seahorses form monogamous pairs. Mating seahorses often entwine prehensile tails in some form of bonding display. At least it seems so. For certain, though, the males provide the prenatal care in this family of fishes. Often in fishes providing some sort of parental care, males guard eggs and young. Seahorses just take such care to an extreme. During an elaborate courtship dance, the female passes her eggs to the male who fertilizes them and then incubates them in the enclosed pouch on his belly. Within the pouch, oxygen is provided to developing eggs by way of a capillary network, and nutrients are transferred, as well. The male controls the pouch's environment so that it becomes more and more like seawater. After the eggs hatch, the young seahorses are pumped out through a small hole in the front of the pouch in an action that looks much like the pangs of childbirth on the part of the male. Soon after the male gives birth, the female seahorse comes around, and the process begins anew. Seahorses produce much smaller broods than most fish, but their remarkable means of doing so assures larger and better-developed young than many much larger species.

DP/Seapics.com

DP/Seapics.com

Top, right: a bluespotted cornetfish.

Top, left: a trumpetfish.

Cornetfishes

(Family Fistulariidae)

Cornetfishes grow much larger than trumpetfishes, up to six feet in length. A long filament, often as long as the fish's body, extends from the tail fin and is lined with sensory pores. Scientists speculate that this filament may be used to detect prey. Cornetfishes swim over sea-grass beds and patch reefs more frequently than trumpetfishes do and venture onto deeper reefs only occasionally. Cornetfishes feed on small fishes and crustaceans.

Two cornetfishes are found in Florida's waters, though neither are considered common. The more common bluespotted cornetfish inhabits patch reefs and sea-grass beds, sometimes swimming in small schools. The rare red cornetfish usually lives over soft bottoms at depths over 30 feet.

Trumpetfishes

(Family Aulostomidae)

Trumpetfishes were so named for the trumpet-like shape the fish take on when they open their mouths. These oddly-shaped reef dwellers grow as long as 32 inches in tropical and subtropical oceans around the world. They hide among coral outcroppings, or even behind the bodies of larger fish, and ambush unsuspecting fishes and crustaceans, sucking them into their mouths in a manner called "pipette feeding."

The trumpetfish is Florida's only member of this small family. Growing up to 30 inches long, the solitary trumpetfish often aligns itself vertically with gorgonians (whip corals) and drifts in this position. It also may sneak up on its prey by swimming behind large fishes. These strategies (and its ability to change color) make trumpetfish difficult to see—good for trumpetfish, bad for its prey. The trumpetfish is commonly found on coral reefs in Florida and in the western Atlantic.

DEAD ZONES

A famous "dead zone" covers almost 7,000 square miles off the coasts of Texas and Louisiana, not all the time, but frequently enough to be recognized by name. This dead zone doesn't result from offshore dumping of hazardous wastes, or from ocean fissures spewing out toxic gasses. The Mississippi River dumps into the Gulf of Mexico huge amounts of water laden with nutrients drained from the farms of America's Midwest. This nutrient-rich water fuels a great bloom of phytoplankton which leads to a depletion of dissolved oxygen in this area---the dead zone. In this zone, larger aquatic life, such as fishes, cannot survive.

Florida experiences its own version of dead zones, though on a much smaller scale. Such dead zones occur ofen enough to be identified repeatedly in Tampa, Sarasota, and Florida bays, and the Indian River Lagoon. At times, usually in summer, oxygen levels reach such low points that these areas can't support most marine life. Organisms that can swim away, such as most fish, do just that. Those that cannot, such as many of the small organisms living on the bottom, simply die. The areas appear lifeless, although they are teeming with microscopic life.

Excess nutrients entering these bays stimulate extensive blooms of phytoplanton. The phytoplankton, often considered a type of algae, produce oxygen through photosynthesis, but this oxygen remains near the water's surface. As the algae die, they sink to the bottom. There, bacteria decompose the dead cells, depleting the oxygen near the bottom in the process.

Florida Bay and the Keys are experiencing another kind of dead zone. A series of natural and human-influenced events began in the 1980s and may have led to a massive die-off of sea grasses and bleaching of corals (corals stop growing and turn white). First a fungus spread from Panama into the Caribbean and Gulf, decimating sea urchin populations. Sea urchins have been credited with helping to control algae growth, and it is believed that the killing of so many urchins prepared the way for the algae that began covering the corals and sea grasses. During the 1990s, El Nino events raised summer water temp-eratures above normal and suppressed hurricane activity in the region. Hurricanes flush out Florida Bay. The warmer water appears to have stimulated coral bleaching. Droughts in South Florida and human water usage reduced freshwater input to Florida Bay and the salinity increased. In addition to the die-offs of sea grasses, a dead zone of seveal hundred square miles in the region has been identified.

DP/Seapics.com

Scorpionfishes and Sea Robins

INTRODUCTION TO THE ORDER SCORPAENIFORMES

The families in this order share one unique feature. An extension of one of the bones surrounding the eye crosses the cheek and connects with the front of the gill cover. Other relationships within this order are not so clear.

Scorpionfishes

(Family Scorpaenidae)

This family was named for the venomous glands imbedded at the bases of large dorsal spines, which can inflict painful wounds. Most species are found in relatively shallow water, but one group, the idiotfishes, live on the bottom at depths of 7,000 feet. Scorpion-fishes typically are well-camouflaged, with fleshy tabs on the head and body, and live on the bottom, lying motionless until a small fish or shrimp comes near. Then they leap from ambush and snap up the hapless prey. Scorpionfishes cover the range of marine habitats. In Florida, some species prefer reefs and hard-bottom areas, others frequent sea-grass beds, and even sand.

Florida can count 21 species of scorpionfish among its plethora of fishes. The spotted scorpionfish is considered a dangerous nuisance by anglers because of its venomous spines. The barbfish is common off the Florida Panhandle. The common reef scorpionfish may occupy tide pools, as well as patch reefs.

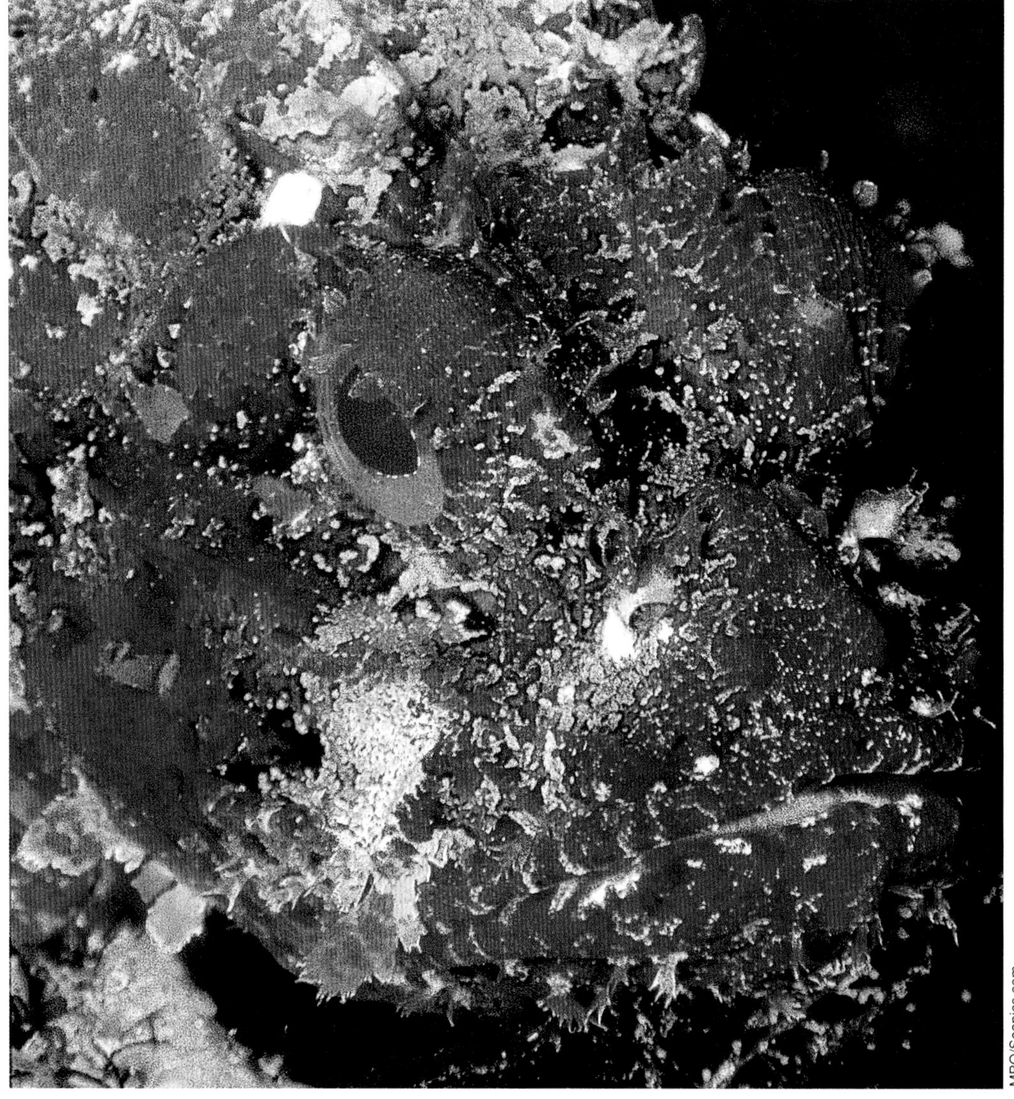

MPO/Seapics.com

Top: **diver and a spotted scorpionfish, the most common scorpionfish around Florida reefs.**

Above: **a close-up of spotted scorpionfish.**

MK/Seapics.com

DP/Seapics.com

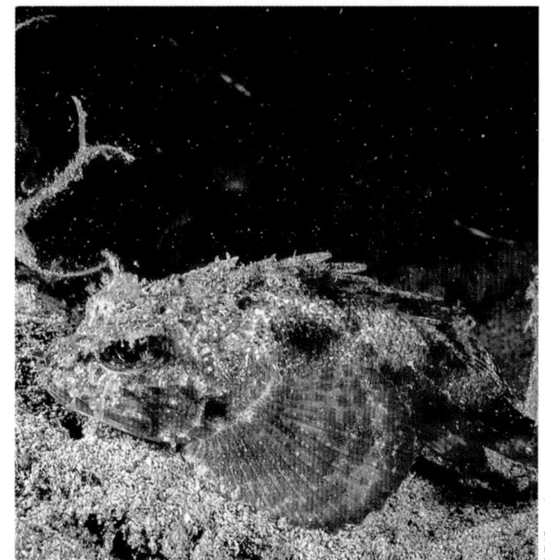

DP/Seapics.com

DP/Seapics.com

Top: a juvenile barbfish.

Middle, right: a mushroom scorpionfish.

Above: a scorpionfish (close-up of its venemous dorsal spines).

Bottom: spotted scorpionfish.

MK/Seapics.com

Searobins

(Family Triglidae)

Searobins are a group of bottom-dwelling, distant relatives of flying gurnards. Like gurnards, searobins have enlarged pectoral fins, but in this family, the lower three rays are not connected by a membrane. Searobins use these rays like fingers to amble along the bottom and probe sediment for food. Searobins prefer shallow areas of sea-grasses, sand, and coral rubble. Rarely are they found on reefs. Like the gurnards, many searobins make sounds, especially during spawning, by using special drumming muscles to vibrate the swim bladder. Numerous spines armor the heads of most searobins.

Of the 100 or so species of searobins, perhaps 15 are found in Florida. The bandtail searobin is distinguished by filaments on its nostril and fleshy tentacles above its eyes. It is distributed widely in Florida but is nowhere abundant. The horned searobin is named for the prominent horn-like projections at each corner of its snout. The northern searobin is found along Florida's east coast.

Top: **a leopard searobin.**

Opposite page:

Top and Bottom: **flying gunards. The huge pectoral fins allow the fish to glide through the water and also make it appear larger to its enemies.**

Flying Gurnards

(Family Dactylopteridae)

Flying gurnards don't really fly but look like they could. Huge pectoral fins are splashed with bright colors on the underside. They may spread their large pectorals and glide along the bottom at shallow to moderate depths. They feed mostly on crustaceans and small fishes. The gurnards' common name derives from the Latin *grunnire*, meaning "to grunt," and refers to the noise they make using their swim bladder.

Oddly enough, Florida's one flying gurnard has sometimes been mistaken for a ray when seen underwater. This shy fish often inhabits sand and sea-grass areas near patch reefs.

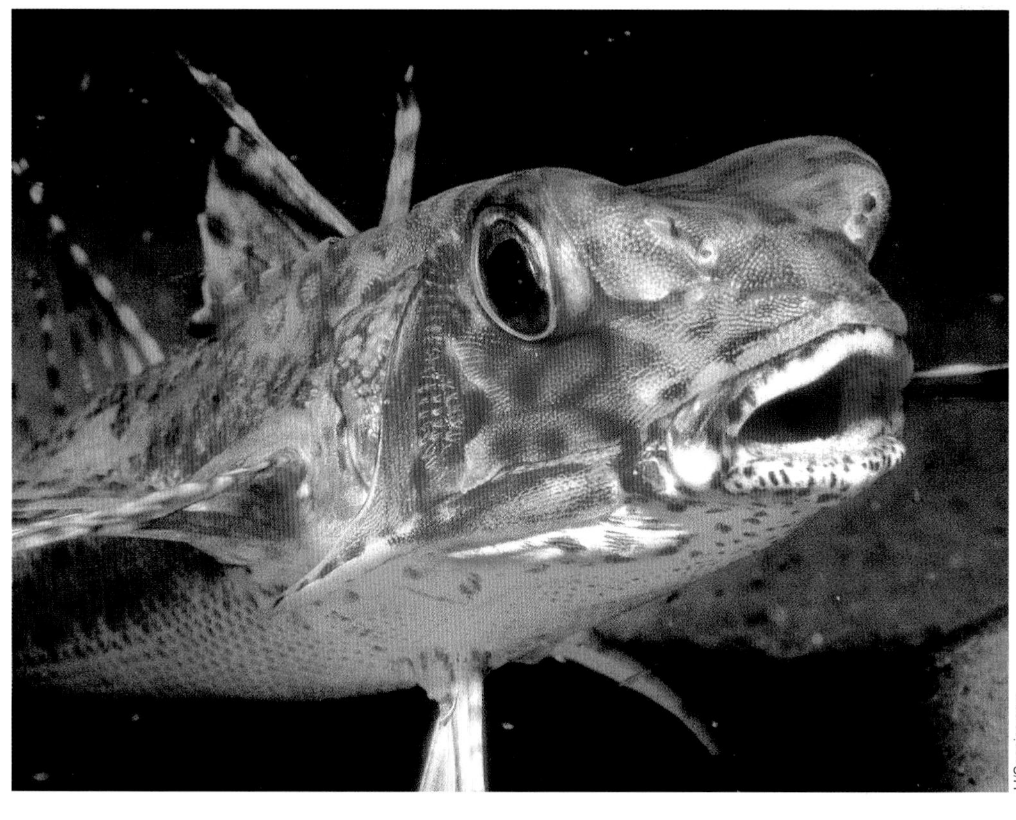

JJ/Seapics.com

Right: **a flying gunard. Note the strong rays of the pectoral fins which give the gunard support as it rests on the bottom.**

DP/Seapics.com

DP/Seapics.com

Perches, Basses, and Their Allies

INTRODUCTION TO THE ORDER PERCIFORMES

The Perciformes are the largest and most diverse order of vertebrates. "Perciform" means "perch-like" and may mislead someone into thinking the members of this order are quite similar. Nothing could be further from the truth. Most species are marine, but several families dominate among the freshwater fish where they are found. In fact, "perches" inhabit just about every kind of aquatic habitat on earth, from cold mountain streams, to sluggish impoundments, to the deep ocean. Their size differences are huge. The smallest "perch:" the marine goby, at .5 inch. The largest: the black marlin, at 14 feet and 2,000 pounds. What about "real" perches? They have their own family, Percidae.

DP/Seapics.com

Snooks

(Family Centropomidae)

"Snook" is almost synonymous with South Florida's backwater fishing. These are fish of the inshore lagoons and lower reaches of rivers, especially around mangroves. They live mostly in salt water at depths less than 60 feet, but all species will enter fresh water, particularly during the winter. Snook are tropical fish that can't tolerate water temperatures below 60° F. and often seek warmer water in rivers and canals in cold weather. Even so, sudden drops in temperature in South Florida have caused fish kills that included numerous snook and other tropical species.

Snook, or *robalo* in Spanish, are easily recognized by their low-slung, pike-like jaws and black lateral lines. They prey aggressively on other fishes, shrimp, and crabs. Snook are summer spawners and often congregate around passes and inlets of Central and South Florida during those months.

VU - KL

Four species of snook inhabit Florida's coastal waters. The largest, the common snook, ranges as far north as the Crystal River in west-central Florida. Though five to ten pounds seems to be the usual weight range for common snook, they are known to reach up to 50 pounds. This snook sometimes ventures onto shallow nearshore reefs. Anglers have dubbed this popular sport fish "linesider" due to its prominent, black lateral line. This species was once fished to the brink of a population collapse. Fortunately, strict government regulation and angler awareness allowed Florida's best-known snook to recover.

The three other species of snook in Florida are even more tropical in nature than common snook, normally inhabiting a limited range in the inshore waters of South Florida. The fat snook rarely exceeds 20 inches and has the tips of its pelvic fins reaching its anus. Fat snook enter freshwater bodies more commonly than do the other snooks. The 16 to 18 inch tarpon snook is rare along Florida's Gulf coast but has been found as far north as the Panhandle. In the little snook, the second anal spine is very long and stout, giving this fish its second common name of "swordspine" snook. Adult swordspine snook mature at less than twelve inches.

***Top and above:* snook. Note the underslung jaw and the prominent black lateral line that looks like a racing stripe.**

Temperate Basses

(Family Moronidae)

This small family of freshwater and anadromous fishes includes members in the temperate waters of Europe, North America, and northern Africa.

The striped bass, or striper, is Florida's only native temperate bass and is fairly common in northern Florida. Two disjunct populations of striped bass occur along Florida's coasts, one in the Atlantic and one in the Gulf.

Stripers are anadromous fish which live most of their lives in salt water but ascend freshwater streams to spawn. It's at this point these fish have run into trouble. Dams have prevented these fish from completing their spawning runs in two of their principal rivers. The Rodman Dam blocks stripers from the portion of the Ocklawaha River that is their prime spawning area in the St. Johns watershed. The Jim Woodruff Dam prevents stripers from reaching the upper Apalachicola River in the west.

When striped bass can complete their spring spawning run, they scatter large numbers of small eggs in shoal areas of rivers. The eggs are slightly negatively buoyant and are carried downstream. A steady flow of water is critical to prevent the eggs from settling to the bottom where they would be suffocated in the sediment.

VU - PC

The Florida Fish and Wildlife Conservation Commission has artificially produced a hybrid involving female striped bass and males of non-native white bass. This sterile sunshine bass has been stocked as a sport fish in Florida. Striped bass, themselves, have been widely stocked as sport fish outside their natural range, and there are landlocked populations of stripers in several states and in Florida's Lake Seminole. White bass in the Apalachicola River are introduced.

Top: **a striped bass.**

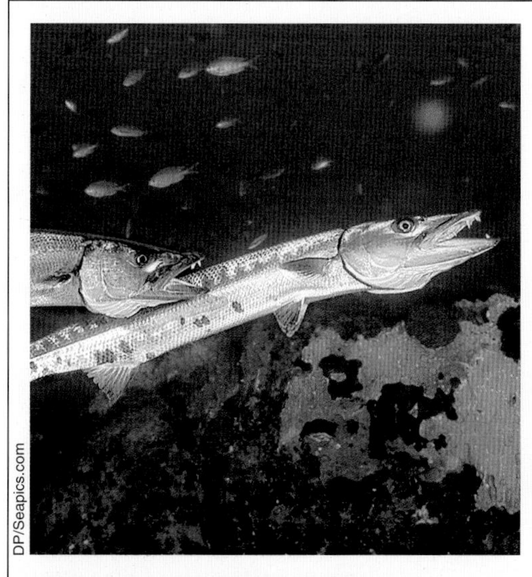

DP/Seapics.com

DP/Seapics.com

HOW FISH REPRODUCE

Spawning in fishes ranges from tumultuous to peaceful, relecting the great variety of fishes. It may involve elaborate courtship or seem almost hit-and-run in its speed and simplicity. The mode of reproduction, however, follows one of two paths, egg-laying, or livebearing.

In egg-layers, the female expels the eggs from her body. The eggs then develop outside her body. Livebearers, as their name suggests, give birth to young that began life within the female's body. The vast majority of fishes lay eggs, however, among the cartilaginous fishes, such as sharks, livebearing is common (see page 11 for details of shark reproduction).

Many fishes simply scatter their eggs and leave them to drift and become part of the vast quantities of plankton. Other species build nests in the sediments where they lay their eggs and guard them from predators. Still other fishes deposit their eggs in cavities or on the underside of leaves of aquatic plants. A few fishes brood their eggs inside their mouths and may even allow the tiny fry to scoot back in when danger threatens. There are many other reproductive strategies.

Hybridization between closely related species is an important part of the pet fish industry. New varieties mean expanded markets. However, hybrids occur in the wild, too. Usually, hybrid fishes show some characteristics that are intermediate between the two parent species.

Top of box, left: **great barracudas bare their teeth during a courtship display.**

Top of box, right: **the female orange-lined cardinalfish (an Indo-Pacific species) extrudes her eggs while the male swims above and releases his milt (sperm) to fertilize them.**

DP/Seapics.com

Sunfishes and Black Basses

(Family Centrarchidae)

The centrarchids are probably the most popular freshwater game fish in the American South, particularly Florida. Anglers spend countless hours and dollars pursuing "bream," crappies, and largemouth bass.

These fish are true Americans; they do not occur naturally anywhere outside North America. A few species have been introduced into other temperate parts of the world, such as Europe and Japan, and state governments have extended their range pretty much across the US, sometimes to the detriment of certain native fish populations.

Almost all centrarchids build and guard nests. Normally the males construct shallow, circular depressions in the sand or gravel, usually in or near vegetated areas. Spawning occurs during the day, with eggs often being laid by a succession of females. Several sunfish species carry out similar breeding behavior and may construct nests relatively close to one another. When this happens, accidental hybridization is fairly common. Such hybridization is rare in Florida. A possible reason is that Florida's sandy soil allows run-off to settle out of water more quickly restoring visibility and allowing the fish to identify members of their own species more easily.

Centrarchids are primarily sight feeders, most active during early morning and evening before dark. All species feed on fishes, insects, and crusaceans, but the exact make-up of their diet varies somewhat by species.

Most of the 22 species of Florida centrarchids are small panfish and at least 18 of these are native. The genus *Lepomis* includes popular species of "bream," such as the bluegill, named for the distinct blue sheen of the males' gill covers and mouth. The redear sunfish, or shellcracker, is unusual in its preference for molluscs. In the aptly-named redbreast sunfish, the breeding male displays a bright orange breast and belly, and orange fins. The warmouth doesn't look much like the others in the genus, being chunkier with a larger head and mouth quite capable of swallowing a surprisingly large meal. Other *Lepomis* sunfish in Florida include spotted sunfish, or stumpknocker, dollar sunfish, and the introduced green sunfish.

The black crappie, or speck, is the only crappie native to Florida. It has been introduced so widely throughout the US that its original range is difficult to determine accurately. It eats mostly fish and particularly likes threadfin shad where available. Black crappie often school around underwater structure and are gregarious spawners. One female may lay between 11,000 and 188,000 eggs. Few crappie live beyond five years. The oldest black crappie in Florida was at the ripe old age of eleven.

The blackbanded sunfish and bluespotted sunfish prefer the mud-bottomed pools of sluggish creeks, ponds, and backwaters.

WNR

VU - GM

***Top:* a redbreast sunfish. This species is more strictly confined to large streams than other Florida sunfishes. Its range is mostly the Atlantic coast from Florida north to Maine.**

***Center:* a warmouth.**

***Bottom:* a bluegill (bream).**

Top: sunfish.

Above: a white crappie (speck). Not native to Florida, but a few have been introduced.

Above: a black crappie.

Above: a dollar sunfish.

Above: a mud sunfish.

WNR

Above: a longear sunfish.

SNEAKY LITTLE FELLOWS

Bluegills, like other bream, spawn in individual nests located closely together in "beds." In general, the biggest males get the girls. Several females may deposit eggs in the same nest to be fertilized by the male guarding that nest. Usually, the larger males dominate the best locations, and territorial males drive away smaller males. Not to be outdone, though, the smaller males have devised some clever tricks. Where there's a will, there's a way; these small but determined males spawn in the nest of one of the big boys. They can't just swim in and start courting, though. That would invite the displeasure of the larger male that built the nest. Instead of the direct approach, these smaller male bluegills look for the opportunity to be "sneakers" or "satellites" in their quests for spawning partners.

Sneakers do just what their name suggests. They sneak into a nest and quickly fertilize eggs while the territorial male's attention is directed toward his mate of the moment. Satellite males go even further with their subterfuge. They mimic females and, thus, are allowed into the nest.

VU - FR

Above: a bluespotted sunfish.

VU - GABISCO

Above: a green sunfish.

BM

Above: a blackbanded sunfish.

BM

Above: a banded sunfish.

Black Basses

(Family Centrarchidae)

The black basses are among the most popular sport fishes and, for this reason, have been widely introduced around the world. The largemouth bass includes two distinct subspecies. The larger subspecies is endemic to the Florida peninsular and has been stocked elsewhere in the US. This bass is the largest of the sunfish family. Males seldom exceed 16 inches, but females frequently exceed 22 inches. Largemouth bass build 20-inch to 30-inch saucer-shaped nests by placing their lower jaw near the bottom and rotating around this position. A female deposits up to 100,000 eggs into the nest. Largemouths are true opportunists when it comes to eating. Adults go after fishes, crustaceans, insects, frogs, small turtles, and even baby ducks. Their name fits: "large mouth."

Other members of the genus *Micropterus* call Florida home, too. The Suwannee bass was restricted to the Suwannee and Ochlockonee rivers and their tributaries in Florida and Georgia, and has recently been introduced into the Wacissa River System. This bass prefers a faster current than largemouth bass, but in the Ichetucknee River both species are found. The Suwannee bass has been designated a "Species of Special Concern" in Florida because of its limited range. It is even less common in Georgia.

MK/Seapics.com

Top: a black sea bass.

DP/Seapics.com

Above: a sand bass.

WNR

Above: a shadow bass (juvenile).

VU - MASLOWSKI

Above: a largemouth bass.

DP/Seapics.com

Above: a harlequin bass.

MK/Seapics.com

Above: a bank sea bass.

LM/Seapics.com

Top: a largemouth bass.

Right: this feeding photo shows why the largemouth bass is known to anglers as the "bucketmouth."

Bottom, left: the eggs of a largemouth bass on a nest.

Bottom, right: a largemouth bass goes after its underwater prey.

Opposite page: a largemouth bass goes for the angler's bait.

WNR

BASS-FISHING MADNESS: THE ALLURE OF AMERICA'S MOST POPULAR GAMEFISH

The largemouth bass is found all across America but thrives and reaches its largest size in warm climates where food is available year-round. The largemouth loves an underwater environment with lots of cover, which mean snags for the fisherman. But, millions of bass fisherman take that in stride as they spend their money on high-tech gear including rods and reels, lures, electronic underwater detectors, bass boats, trailers, and four-wheel drives, not to mention accessories such as caps and "kiss my bass" t-shirts. Bass fishing tournaments with large cash prizes abound.

The allure of the largemouth bass can be attributed to its voracious feeding habits which include bone-jarring strikes at almost anything edible, its fighting spirit, its size and strength, its high intelligence and widespread availability.

LM/Seapics.com

WNR

Pygmy Sunfishes

(Family Elassomatidae)

This small family with a single genus is native to the quiet, weedy waters of the southeastern US. The pygmy sunfishes feed by sight on crustaceans, mollusks, and insect larvae. They do not construct nests for spawning, but they do defend territories and guard eggs, which are usually attached to dense vegetation. These fishes seldom live longer than one year. Their common name describes this family accurately; they stay well under two inches in length.

Four pygmy sunfishes occur in Florida, one not yet named. The Everglades pygmy sunfish is actually more common in Florida outside the Everglades. During the breeding season, males become shiny black with bright, iridescent blue bars on their sides. Other species include the Okefenokee pygmy sunfish and banded pygmy sunfish, both common in northern Florida.

Below: **an Everglades pygmy sunfish (male in breeding colors).**

Below, left: **an Okefenokee pygmy sunfish.**

VU - FR

WNR

PUGNACIOUS PYGMIES

Pygmy sunfish have been identified as neotenous fish (capable of being sexually mature as juveniles). Maybe that explains the youthful bravado of territorial males as they guard their chosen spawning site. When another male, or even a nongravid female, invades the territorial male's spawning area, the territorial male launches into a threat display.

The territorial male swims fairly close to the intruder and spreads his fins wide, rapidly beating his tail and pectoral fins. His color intensifies, and he may turn himself broadside to the intruder, perhaps to present a larger image to the fish that entered his territory. If all these tricks fail, he moves in closer and strikes at the invader.

Perches (darters)

(Family Percidae)

When is a perch not a perch? "Perch" is applied to dozens of freshwater and saltwater fishes, but it correctly refers only to members of the strictly freshwater Percidae. The best-known perches — walleye, sauger, and yellow perch — do not live in Florida. However, the family is represented in Florida by 17 darter species, the North American group that constitutes the bulk of the perch family. Most darters live in riffles, which are areas of fast-flowing, well-oxygenated water in rivers and streams. They are small fish, usually less than eight inches, and often live in very restricted habitats. Because of their restricted habitats, numerous darters have been classified as "threatened" or "endangered" under the federal Endangered Species Act.

The percids are mostly carnivores that feed by sight. The darters eat small fishes and invertebrates.

Darters spawn primarily during the day and provide varying degrees of parental care, depending on species. Many darters develop incredibly beautiful colors during spawning times.

Though some species enjoy a wide distribution, numerous others have extremely limited ranges. For instance, the Okaloosa darter lives in only seven small creeks in Florida's western Panhandle.

The perch family is large with over 180 species. Over 84 species live in Tennessee alone. In contrast, perhaps 18 percids are native to Florida of which one, the yellow perch, is no longer found in the state. All 16 natives are darters. Only four of these have been found east of the Apalachicola River. The tessellated darter is common along the Atlantic Coast north from Georgia. In Florida, it is found only in the lower Ocklawaha River, a tributary of the St. Johns River.

Other darters in Florida include the brown darter of north-central Florida and the Panhandle; Gulf darter of the western Panhandle east to the Ocklawhaha River drainage; and southern logperch. The most common and widespread darter in Florida is the blackbanded darter, which ranges from the Panhandle into central Florida.

VU - FR

Above: **a speckled darter.**

WNR

Above: an Okaloosa darter.

WNR

Right: **a brown darter.**

DP/Seapics.com

Sea Basses and Groupers
(Family Serranidae)

Groupers and sea basses form a large and diverse family. Also included in this family are hinds, hamlets, coneys, and soapfishes. Many are highly valued food fish in various parts of the world. On the sea bed of earth's warm oceans, however, groupers and sea basses are vital predators. Serranids are carnivores, with the smallest species feeding on zooplankton and larger species feeding on a variety of fishes and invertebrates. Groupers, in particular, are solitary, voracious predators that live near the bottom. They look far from sleek and agile, but groupers can cover short distances rapidly. They also can expand huge mouths so quickly they create a great suction from which prey cannot escape. Groupers' often interrupted pattern of color and markings help them blend into surroundings and make ambush of prey even more effective.

This family is abundant in tropical and subtropical seas, most often around coral reefs, patch reefs, deep channels, and other structure. At least 65 species occur in Florida. Some species live at moderate depths offshore. Others prefer shallow bays and jetties. Some wear bright colors, but others appear more somber. Several species even display different colors in deep water and shallow water, possibly because their melanin pigment doesn't develop as well in poor light. Some species spawn in pairs at dusk. Others, such as the Nassau grouper, come from great distances to form large concentrations in specific locations. Serranids run the gamut of sizes, too, ranging from pygmy sea bass, Florida's smallest seabass at two inches, to the giant Goliath grouper (formerly known as the jewfish) at about 700 pounds.

Some larger groupers can be hard to distinguish because they radically change both colors and markings, presumably to fit in better with surroundings. Examples are yellowfin grouper and yellowmouth grouper, which cross paths off southeastern Florida.

Soapfish were once classified in a separate family but are generally considered as part of the seabass family today. They get their common name from the toxic mucus covering their bodies, or more precisely from its effect. When soapfish are frightened or handled, the mucus produces bad-tasting, soap-like bubbles. Predators learn to avoid these fishes. The largest Atlantic species is the greater soapfish, a common soapfish along Florida's East Coast and the Keys, where it is found along shorelines and on reefs.

Top and bottom: **a Goliath grouper (formerly called the jewfish).**

DDM/Seapics.com

JJ/Seapics.com

Above: a Naussau grouper.

DDM/Seapics.com

Above: a marbled grouper.

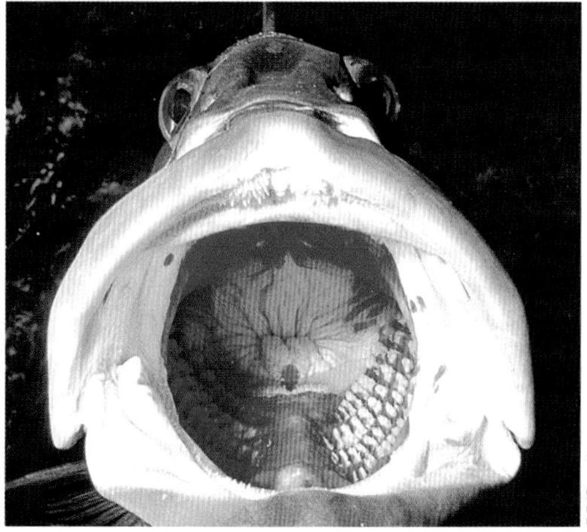

DP/Seapics.com

Above: a Naussau grouper "yawning."

JJ/Seapics.com

Above: a coney.

DP/Seapics.com

Above: a tiger grouper.

Below: a black grouper.

DP/Seapics.com

THEIR OWN WORST ENEMY?

Groupers lend themselves to over fishing. They yield large filets, making them popular food. Divers can easily approach many groupers, making them easy targets for spear fishing. In addition, groupers live near the top of the food chain, meaning only a few live at any one locality. In fact, only one or two very large groupers may occupy a reef. Groupers are slow growing, late maturing fish, needing five years or more to mature sexually and living 25 to 40 years. Consequently, no reef has a large population of groupers. An exception occurs with a few species during spawning. Like Nassau groupers, giant groupers (formerly jewfish) form large spawning aggregations. Such concentrations are so vulnerable to over exploitation, the state now protects goliath groupers from both recreational and commercial fishing.

CH/Seapics.com

DP/Seapics.com

Top: indigo hamlets.
Center: a barred hamlet.
Bottom: a shy hamlet.

MK/Seapics.com

MC/Seapics.com

BOY OR GIRL?

As if the sea basses weren't diverse enough already, they also are hermaphroditic—but not all in the same manner. Some species have both male and female reproductive organs that function simultaneously. Other species begin life as females and transform into males sometime later. It gets stranger, still. Individuals in some species can function first as one sex, then as the other a few minutes later. Some species live in harems of one male and several females. In these species, if the male is removed, a large female will assume the male's role and transform into a functional male within a few days. All the seabasses do share one spawning characteristic, though. They perform their courtship rituals whether they are one sex or both.

Top: a greater soapfish.

Right: a red hind.

Below: a rock hind, which can usually be found resting on deep coral reefs in the Gulf of Mexico.

Opposite page, top: graybys

DP/Seapics.com

MK/Seapics.com

MU/Seapics.com

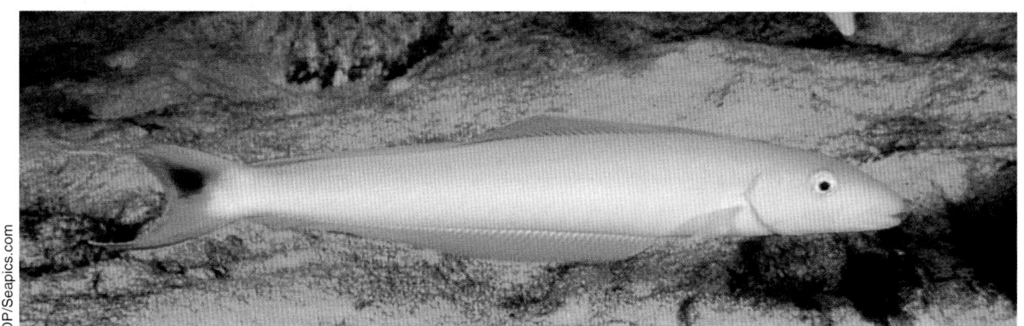

DP/Seapics.com

Above: **a sand tilefish.**

Tilefishes

(Family Malacanthidae)

Tilefishes are a diverse family, at one time divided into two families. Most species live along hard, sandy bottoms in the rather deep water along the slope of the continental shelf, and there they construct burrows. These wary fish often hover above their burrows by undulating their long dorsal and anal fins, quickly disappearing back inside at the least disturbance.

The anchor tilefish is thought to be restricted to the Gulf. The sand tilefish is found along both coasts of Florida and builds nests of small coral rubble around its burrow, and nests may reach several feet across. Like any proud homeowner, it spends much of its time rearranging the coral piece-by-piece. When alarmed, this tilefish darts into a hole beneath its nest.

TILEFISH HELP SHAPE THEIR WORLD

Tilefish burrows have helped shape the ocean floor, essentially by undermining it. Their burrows may dominate extensive areas of the continental slope, and multiple burrows sometimes open into the same large cavern. The fish excavate with their mouths by removing mouthfuls of clay as they dig and depositing the clay near the burrow. In addition, swimming activity by fish inside the burrow washes out finer sediments. No matter how the burrows are made, tilefishes don't live in them alone. The burrows are often enlarged by crabs, and some burrows may link with others. The resulting honeycomb structure sometimes weakens the sea floor to the point it collapses, producing pits several feet deep.

Bluefish

(Family Pomatomidae)

Named for its bluish coloration, the bluefish is common along both coasts of Florida. Bluefish travel in schools in which all individuals are approximately the same size. Juveniles venture inshore into estuaries while larger adults remain offshore. Bluefish make long migrations following the warming waters north in summer and retreating back south in fall. Bluefish are voracious feeders, violently attacking schools of smaller fishes, and are said to kill more than they can eat. Bluefish have attacked swimmers, leaving severe lacerations from their sharp teeth. Anglers seek bluefish for their hard strikes, strong runs, and tasty flesh. The novelist, John Hersey, wrote a book entitled *Blues,* in large part about the nature of this fish.

MSTRICKLAND/Seapics.com

Above: **the wrasse basslet is an attactive small species of the sebass family, but is very seldom seen since it is found around deep offshore reefs and rocky ledges from North Carolina to Mexico.**

Remoras

(Family Echeneidae)

Remoras and sharksuckers hitch rides on sharks, rays, bony fishes, turtles, and even ships, thanks to the flat sucking disc on top of the head. The sucking disc is actually a modified dorsal fin. Within the sucker are pairs of plates that look somewhat like the slats in venetian blinds. These fish can operate these plates to create a vacuum between themselves and their host.

Typically members of this family feed on fish and bits of their host's prey. Some species also act as cleaner fish, at times, eating parasites from the host's body.

There are only eight species of this family which can be found in Florida's coastal waters. The spearfish remora favors its namesake.

The remora attaches to just about anything handy. The equally common and less particular sharksucker strays into estuaries. The whalesucker remora attaches itself to dolphins and whales.

DP/Seapics.com

DP/Seapics.com

The name "remora" comes from a Latin word meaning "delay." Remoras and sharksuckers may be a bit of hindrance to their hosts. These fish can swim quite well on their own, but prefer to ride for free.

As an example of the power of the sucking disk, it has been reported that natives in some Caribbean islands attach a line to a remora's tail and release it in the water near a sea turtle. After the remora races over and attaches itself to the turtle, the line is pulled in and the turtle captured.

Top and left: **sharksuckers. In the top photo, the sharksucker is attached to a turtle.**

Cobias

(Family Rachycentridae)

The cobia is the only member of this family. Cobia are closely related to remoras and especially resemble them as juveniles. However, cobia show little resemblance to any other fish.

Cobia are widely distributed in warm seas around the world. Small cobia enter saltier bays during the summer. They are large fish, ranging from 50 to 100 pounds or more. They congregate around marine structures such as buoys, pilings, and patch reefs. In a style reminiscent of sharks, cobia swim with their pectoral fins stiffly extended. They eat crabs, squid, and fishes.

PC/Seapics.com

Basslets

(Family Grammatidae)

Basslets make up a small family of small fishes. Growing from one to four inches in length, basslets generally prefer deeper reefs, though some species also inhabit rocky shorelines. Basslets display vivid coloration. All ten species of basslets are confined to tropical waters of the western Atlantic, and Florida can claim three species, two native, none common in the state. Shy little fishes, basslets like the security of caves and crevices of reefs. There they commonly swim upside down, apparently orienting themselves to the roofs of their caves, or overhangs, as if those were the sea floor. Even when outside their caves, they may swim at a 45 degree angle. Basslets feed primarily on small shrimps, crabs and other crustaceans. Male basslets build nests of algae and bits of plants.

The fairy basslet, or royal gramma, is a Caribbean species, possibly introduced into Florida in the vicinity of Miami. The rare threeline basslet is a tiny, very reclusive reef dweller.

MPO/Seapics.com

Top: **two fairy baslets (royal gramma or *Gramma loreto*) sparring.**

Jawfishes

(Family Opistognathidae)

Jawfishes live in burrows in sand adjacent to reefs and place stones, like small walls, around their burrows. Sometimes jawfish occupy reef crevices, but even here they like to add some small stones. Some jawfish often hover a few inches above burrows, while others usually wait in their burrows to ambush prey that happens by. Jawfishes are egg layers, and the male carries the eggs in his mouth until they hatch. There are about 90 species of jawfishes, with perhaps eight in Florida.

The yellowhead jawfish is common in shallow waters of southeastern Florida and the Keys. It hovers above its burrow and retreats into it tail first when frightened. The less common banded jawfish of southernmost Florida usually keeps to its burrow with just its head poking out.

JW/Seapics.com

Above: **a male yellowhead jawfish mouth-brooding eggs.**

MK/Seapics.com

Right: **a banded jawfish also incubating a cluster of eggs in its mouth.**

DP/Seapics.com

Bigeyes

(Family Priacanthidae)

Bigeyes are named for their…well, big eyes. They also have big mouths, but "Bigmouths" must not have appealed to those who named this family. Most of the family sport similar colors of pink, red, or orange and live over hard bottoms, often in deep water. Though some may move into shallow waters during the spring and summer, all bigeyes seek protection in rocky ledges and crevices. There are 18 species of bigeyes known, with three or four in Florida.

The bigeye is a common Florida bigeye found on both coasts. Small groups drift in the current above reefs 66 to over 600 feet deep. This affinity for deep reefs, together with its uniform red to salmon color, distinguish the bigeye from the similar glasseye snapper, which prefers shallow reefs, and has silver bars on its back. A much rarer fish in Florida is the short bigeye.

Top: **a glasseye snapper.**

Middle, right: **a short bigeye.**

Bottom: **a bigeye.**

MP/Seapics.com

DL

DP/Seapics.com

Cardinalfishes

(Family Apogonidae)

Because of their small size, mostly under four inches, the cardinalfishes' large, dark eyes look even larger. The Apogonidae are primarily nocturnal reef fishes, remaining in caves or crevices during the day, often in close association with corals. Some species (none in our part of the world) enter brackish or fresh water on occasion. True freshwater species are found in Australia, New Guinea, and certain Pacific Islands. Mouthbrooding of eggs by males has been found in studied species, and perhaps others in this family do the same. A few species possess a luminescent organ in their abdomen.

Eighteen of over 200 species in this family are found in Florida, including three genera: *Phaeoptyx, Astrapogon,* and *Apogon.* The belted cardinalfish is a common South Florida resident, often seen on night dives around shallower reefs. This two to three inch fish likes to hover amid the spines of the long-spined sea urchin. The flamefish has a much wider distribution in Florida than the belted cardinalfish and sometimes can be found around pilings in shallow water and on deep reefs. The flamefish may be the most common cardinalfish in Florida. The conchfish typically lives within the mantle of the Queen conch.

DP/Seapics.com

BH/Seapics.com

***Top:* a flamefish.**

***Above:* a blackfin cardinalfish**

***Left:* a bigtooth cardinalfish.**

MU/Seapics.com

Dolphinfishes
(Mahi-Mahi, or Dorado)
(Family Coryphaenidae)

Dolphins are marine mammals of Hollywood and Seaworld fame. They should not be confused with the fish of the same name with which they have no connection. These dolphinfishes, or dorados, are a small family of only two species of pelagic fishes ranging in all warm seas. The dolphinfishes are well-known for striking, iridescent beauty and ability to change colors rapidly. Since nobody wants to be caught eating Flipper, many Florida seafood purveyors have adopted the Hawaiian name for this fish, Mahi-mahi.

Dolphin often follow ships and congregate beneath floating objects at sea, especially sargassum mats. Commonly these groups contain only one or two males, or bulls, but numerous females. Males can be distinguished easily by their steep, almost vertical forehead.

Both species of dolphinfishes are found in Florida, usually in offshore waters. The dolphinfish is larger and more commonly seen. It grows to about six feet in length, generally lives closer to the surface, and ventures into inshore waters more often. Dolphinfishes live short lives, surviving only two or three years. The pompano dolphinfish may reach three feet.

DP/Seapics.com

MU/Seapics.com

Top, bottom, and above: **several views of the dolphinfish. Note the beautiful irisdescent colors for which this fish is famous.**

DP/Seapics.com

Top, left: **a dark-phase bar jack follows a feeding stingray to scavenge scraps.**

Center: **one member of a pair of barjacks adopts a dark color phase during courtship.**

Bottom: **crevalle jacks**

Jacks, Scads, and Pompanos

(Family Carangidae)

This rather large family of about 140 species ranges around the world in temperate and tropical seas.

The leatherjacket, or leatherjack, favors rather turbid water along sandy beaches, bays, and river mouths. The sharp anal spines of this small jack contain venom and can inflict a bloody and painful cut. juvenile leatherjacks use their incisor-like teeth to serve as cleaners for other species of fish. As they mature, their teeth become more conical, and their diet changes to small fish and crustaceans.

DP/Seapics.com

DP/Seapics.com

Crevalle jacks, are the most common jacks of inshore waters, found in bays, rivers, and along beaches. Juveniles and young adults tend to school, while large fish often travel alone in the open waters well offshore. At times, schools of jacks will drive schools of bait fish against sea walls and engage in a feeding frenzy that boils the surface.

Less common than the crevalle jack, horse-eye jack swim in schools in the open water over reefs. The young of this jack and the crevalle jack are often found together in shallower water and are easily confused. The horse-eye jack's large eye gives it another common name, "bigeye jack."

The round scad, or cigarfish, is a small, poorly known but widespread jack. It usually occurs offshore in water up to 300 feet deep, but ventures inshore more often east of the Mississippi River. This plankton feeder consumes a variety of free-swimming invertebrates.

MU/Seapics.com

Jacks, Scads, and Pompanos
(Family Carangidae)

Permit are often confused with pompano, but permit grow much larger, up to three feet or so, with a deeper body. Permit also frequent reefs, while pompano rarely do. Sometimes permit cruise shallow flats searching for small crabs and other invertebrates. The tips of their tail fins stick out of the water as they search the bottom for favorite morsels. Little is known about the permit's life history, but it is believed they spawn offshore. Like others in this genus, young permit occur in the surf, adding to their confusion with pompano.

DP/Seapics.com

The blue runner, or hard-tail, is a common schooling jack fond of open water and smooth bottoms. On the rare occasions that it visits reefs, it usually does so singly or in pairs.

MU/Seapics.com

Top: **a pair of permit courting.**

Center: **blue runners.**

Bottom: **a black jack.**

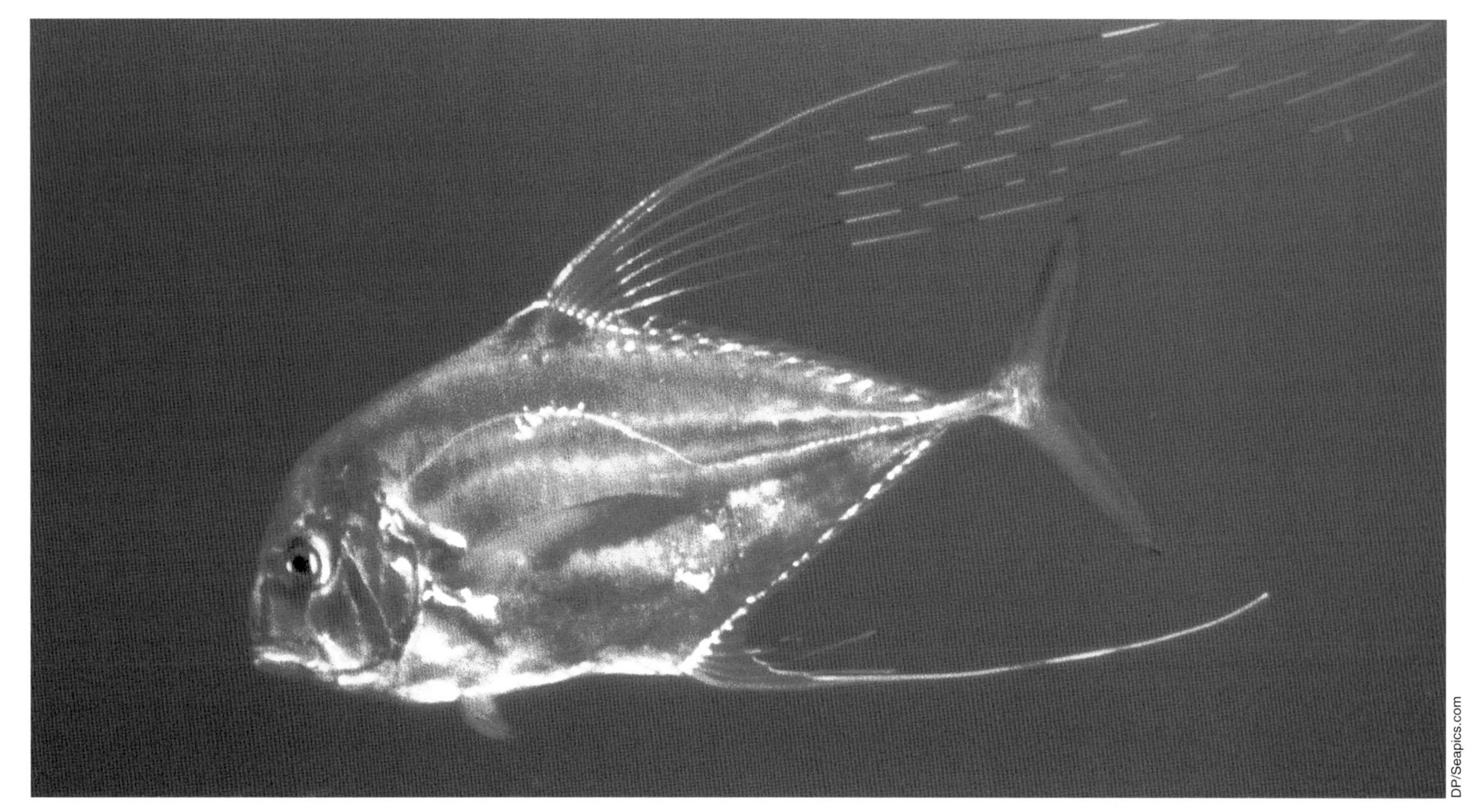

DP/Seapics.com

Pompano schools abound in summer surf, feeding on crustaceans and mollusks. Like many other warm-water fishes, pompano migrate up the coast as the water warms and return south as the water cools. They grow to about 25 inches in length.

Top: **an African pompano photographed off Key Largo.**

Center, left: **an greater amberjack.**

Center, right: **horse-eye jacks.**

Bottom: **cottonmouth jacks.**

DP/Seapics.com

DP/Seapics.com

Pomfrets

(Family Bramidae)

Pomfrets make up a family of oceanic fishes famous for undergoing great changes in body shape as they grow. Generally deep-water fish, the pomfret's tadpole-like larvae hatch from pelagic eggs and grow through several changes, to eventually resemble the butterfishes. Pomfrets make seasonal migrations, apparently tied to water temperatures. Only occasionally do they come inshore and those that do are usually juveniles. Pomfrets eat a variety of small fishes and invertebrates. The lowfin promfret is found near the edge of the continental shelf along Florida's Atlantic coast and in the northern Gulf. The highly migratory keeltail pomfret occurs in much the same waters as sea bream.

MC/Seapics.com

PColla/Seapics.com

Snappers

(Family Lutjanidae)

Snappers and Florida. The two just go together. From the Gulf's deep offshore "snapper banks," to the inshore patch reefs and bridge pilings, to rocks and boat docks in estuaries, 15 species of snappers call Florida home. Most snappers dwell close to bottom around some sort of structure but often feed well away from the bottom. Young frequent shallower water than do the adults. In many species, prominent fang-like teeth jut from the front of the upper jaw, suggesting their predatory nature. Snappers eat a variety of small fishes, crustaceans, and mollusks. They are, themselves, widely sought for food and sport wherever they are found. In fact, their common name comes from their habit of snapping their jaws together when hooked. From time to time, snappers have been implicated in cases of ciguatera poisoning.

Different snappers behave differently on their reefs. Dog, cubera, and mutton snappers are more solitary. Gray, lane, and mahogany snappers are chummier. Yellowtail snappers generally stay well above the reefs in loose aggregations. Schoolmasters troop along in schools and may come quite close to shore around mangroves. Deep-water snappers, such as the red snapper, like to swim so deep that most divers rarely see them. The yellow-striped lane snapper is often abundant on inshore reefs, especially as a juvenile. Gray snappers, very popular with anglers, are commonly called mangrove snappers because as juveniles they are often found around mangroves (as well as reefs). The dog snapper earned its common name from its protruding canine teeth and is less common in Florida than other snappers.

Top: **gray or mangrove snapper.**

Bottom, right: **a mutton snapper.**

Bottom, left: **a lane snapper.**

DP/Seapics.com

DP/Seapics.com

DP/Seapics.com

DDM/Seapics.com

Top: a cubera snapper swimming with reef sharks.

Left: a gray snapper.

Bottom, left: a schoolmaster.

Bottom, right: a yellowtail snapper.

DP/Seapics.com

MU/Seapics.com

Tripletails

(Family Lobotidae)

The tripletail is the only species of this small family in Florida. Three other species exist elsewhere. The rear lobes of the dorsal and anal fins are symmetrical and extend to the tail, giving the appearance of three tails. Even though tripletails are widely distributed in warm seas, even near shore, they are not commonly seen. Young tripletails often associate with floating debris in open water and pilings or similar structure inshore, and are even found in tidal pools along the shore.

Right: **a tripletail. The tripletail is a solitary fish that typically lives underneath floating vegetation or other objects in the open ocean. It is a good sport fish and excellent eating, but is not well known to many fishermen.**

DP/Seapics.com

"SLACKER, THY NAME IS 'TRIPLETAIL'"

Tripletails are robust fish, but they aren't built for speed. That's okay, because their compressed bodies are quite suited for another means of getting around—drifting. Sluggish fish, tripletails often float on their sides near the surface, looking every bit like a piece of trash. They are particularly attracted to buoys and crab trap floats, but they also find shade under sargassum mats and anchored boats at times. Why? No one knows for sure, however, in the open water, any sort of floating cover is attractive to a variety of fishes. If small fish mistakes a floating tripletail for a bit of flotsam, a meal is just a snap away.

PC/Seapics.com

Mojarras

(Family Gerreidae)

One feature that clearly stands out in this family is its extremely protrusible mouth. The jaws can be extended downward and forward, forming a short tube. Mojarras take advantage of their peculiar mouths quite well. Also endowed with very sensitive hearing, mojarras cruise along just a few inches above a sandy bottom and, upon hearing a tasty morsel, quickly extend their mouths and slurp up their meal.

Mojarras inhabit shallow bays, sea-grass beds, and sandy areas near beaches and shallow reefs. Ten species are, at least occasionally, in Florida's coastal waters. The yellowfin mojarra is probably the largest at about 15 inches and is the only mojarra with vertical bars along its sides. It ranges from shallow areas around reefs to sea-grass beds. The shy silver Jenny is more common in the Gulf.

Above: **a yellowfin mojarra. This fish is unlike other local mojarras because it is often found around reefs. Note the vertical bars and the yellow pelvic fins.**

Porgies (sheepshead, pinfish)

(Family Sparidae)

This rather large family of tropical and temperate fishes includes members familiar to almost every Florida saltwater angler. They are held in great distain by some because of their bait-stealing habits. This family's most telltale feature is probably their front teeth. They take one of two forms, either flattened incisors or peg-like canines. Most species are omnivorous, grazing on attached vegetation and munching invertebrates, such as small crabs and shrimps. The porgies are mostly shallow, bottom dwellers. Some species prefer rocks and pilings, while others love the sea-grass beds and mangroves.

The sheepshead is named for its incisors which resemble sheep's teeth. Sheepshead abound in shallow coastal waters and estuaries, even entering rivers. They like hard, vertical structures, such as the higher patch reefs, bridge pilings, and sea walls, where they feed on barnacles, small crabs, and other invertebrates. An attraction to boat basins has caused the demise of many sheepshead in South Florida when they are caught in the shallow water by a sudden freeze.

Pinfish, another well-known but much less popular member of the clan, steal bait throughout coastal Florida. Like most of their kin, pinfish like rocks and pilings, but they also like the sea grass flats, especially as youngsters. Common year-round in much of Florida, pinfish may move offshore during winter in northern parts of the state. Their teeth are flat and incisor-like. True opportunists and voracious feeders, pinfish eat some plant material but mostly target small invertebrates and fishes and, it seems, whatever floats by on a hook.

The saucereye porgy prefers deeper water than many of its family, frequenting reefs and other hard bottom areas down to depths of 250 feet. However, the young often live in sea-grass beds and sandy areas. Its molar-like teeth enable the saucereye to eat sea urchins and brittle stars in addition to porgies' normal invertebrate fare.

DP/Seapics.com

Top: **a sheepshead.**

WNF

Above: **a pinfish from Crystal River.**

DP/Seapics.com

Above: **a saucereye porgy.**

DP/Seapics.com

Grunts

(Family Haemulidae)

Everyone who has dipped a fishing line along Florida's coast has almost certainly caught a grunt. The pigfish is the only common inshore grunt. The lining in the mouth of most species of the genus *Haemulon* is bright red to red-orange.

Grunts received their name from the sound they make grinding together the pharyngeal teeth deep in their throats. This grunting sound is amplified by their swim bladder to a very noticeable level.

During the day, grunts often congregate in the shadows of reefs. At night, they scour sand and sea-grass beds near reefs for invertebrates and small fishes. Grunts make up the greatest fish biomass on certain reefs. However, grunts depend so heavily on the sand and sea-grass beds near reefs that islands having little of these habitats also have fewer grunts. Most grunts feed on small shrimps and crabs and some fishes, and some grunts add algae to their diet.

The largest of Florida's grunts is the black margate, found in South Florida and most of the Gulf. The tomtate is one of the most abundant grunts along Florida's east coast and is also found in the Gulf.

DP/Seapics.com

Top: **bluestriped grunts and longjaw squirrelfish sheltering under brain coral.**

Bottom: **French grunts.**

MPO/Seapics.com

MK/Seapics.com

Top: bluestriped grunts kissing in territorial display.

Left: black margate cleaned by a porkfish.

Below: cottonwick.

Bottom: tomtates.

MK/Seapics.com

DP/Seapics.com

DP/Seapics.com

Drums and Croakers

(Family Sciaenidae)

The large and rather diverse Sciaenidae includes a few small, colorful species. In general, this is a bottom-dwelling, inshore family, with only a few species found around coral reefs. Most species spawn in the Gulf, but the larvae enter brackish bays where they spend their first summer. Many species spend much of their time in brackish water, particularly as juveniles, and occupy a variety of habitats, from mud bottoms to oyster beds to sand.

With many of this family, the mouth gives a clue to their feeding habits. The relatively large mouth with the little fangs of the speckled seatrout reflects the fish-eating nature of this species. Large individuals are believed to feed exclusively on fish. A relatively small, inferior mouth, with enlarged molar-like pharyngeal teeth, identifies the black drum as a bottom-feeding shellfish-lover. It crushes hard-shelled prey with its pharyngeal teeth. By using special muscles to resonate their swim bladders, the sciaenid fishes make the low sounds which give them their common names of "drum" and "croaker."

Other members of this family in Florida include the common high-hat, a small reef-dweller, and the commercially important Atlantic croaker which sometimes enters rivers, most notably the St. Johns.

MK/Seapics.com

VU - DSA

DP/Seapics.com

Top: **a spotted drum, adult.**

Center: **highhat juveniles.**

Above: **a spotted seatrout.**

Right: **a juvenile spotted drum.**

DP/Seapics.com

Goatfishes

(Family Mullidae)

The often colorful goatfishes are common in Florida and dwell on reefs or in the open Gulf. Their most distinctive feature is the pair of long chin barbels they use to probe sand and rubble near reefs for small invertebrates. Often wrasses and other small fishes follow feeding goatfishes to nab any prey that escapes. Goatfishes can change color rapidly, particularly at night, or when being "cleaned" by another fish. Even though adult goatfishes dwell on the bottom, their post-larvae live near the surface and may grow to two or three inches before settling to the bottom.

About 60 species of goatfishes occur in tropical and temperate waters around the world; four are found in Florida. The slender yellow goatfish feeds alone or in small groups, but when not feeding, often swims in large schools over its reef. It is attracted to the shade of sea fans and some of the higher reef structures. The spotted goatfish is one of those species that changes colors dramatically when at a cleaning station being groomed by small cleaner fishes or shrimps. When not feeding, it often rests on the bottom and changes color to match the background.

DP/Seapics.com

DP/Seapics.com

Top: **a yellow goatfish**

Center: **a spotted goatfish**

Bottom: a **spotted goatfish probing for food in sand using its whiskers (barbels) as sensors.**

MU/Seapics.com

Sweepers

(Family Pempheridae)

Sweepers congregate in small groups or large schools, often hovering in the shaded areas of reefs or in caves. They sometimes enter very shallow water. They have large eyes, and are largely nocturnal, feeding on zooplankton.

Worldwide, there are 25 species in this family. The glassy sweeper is one of possibly two sweepers found along Florida's southern coast and often occupies large, shaded holes in reefs. This fish may even be found in the interior of shipwrecks. Glassy sweepers owe their common name to their juveniles, which are so transparent their backbones can be seen.

Butterflyfishes

(Family Chaetodontidae)

The butterflyfishes are small but conspicuous reef dwellers in almost all tropical and warm, temperate marine waters. This family contains some of the most beautiful tropical fish. As colorful as their butterfly namesake, these little jewels flit about the reefs searching for food, sometimes alone, but usually in pairs. Those in pairs keep track of their partners, and those in groups interact with one another as they swim along the reef, much to the delight of divers. When pairs become separated, one partner often swims upward for a better view to locate and rejoin its partner.

Some species have a dark spot near the tail, called a "false eye spot." Many of these same species also have a dark bar, or other marking, obscuring their real eyes, leading to speculation that this pattern confuses predators. Their narrow bodies allow butterflyfishes to escape into crevices in the reefs when alarmed.

The 115 or so butterflyfishes display similar disk-shaped bodies but their coloration often differs remarkably. Even between juvenile and adult in many species, a dramatic change in coloration and pattern takes place. Butterflyfishes vary in size and shape of jaws, too. As in most fishes, the jaws correlate to the food items eaten. Some species have short jaws used to nip coral polyps. Others have long jaws they use like forceps to pick tiny invertebrates from coral crevices or from between spines of sea urchins. In fact, their mouths give this family its name. "Chaetodont" refers to the tiny brush-like teeth common to butterflyfishes. Invertebrates and sometimes algae make up the bulk of the diet of most of this family.

Most butterflyfishes patrol a home territory. Many species form heterosexual pairs that may remain together for life. These egg-layers go through a protracted larval stage lasting in the plankton for as much as two months in some species. The head and body of the distinctive late stage larvae are covered with bony plates. Juveniles of several species look sufficiently different from adults they have been confused as different species.

The longsnout butterflyfish is a fairly common butterflyfish of the deeper reefs off Florida's coast, down 100 to 200 feet. The foureye butterflyfish commonly ventures onto shallow inshore reefs and is Florida's only butterflyfish with converging lines along the sides.

DP/Seapics.com

Above: **four-eye butterflyfishes.**

DP/Seapics.com

Above: **a longsnout butterflyfish.**

DP/Seapics.com

Above: **a spotfin butterflyfish.**

DP/Seapics.com

Above: **a banded butterflyfish.**

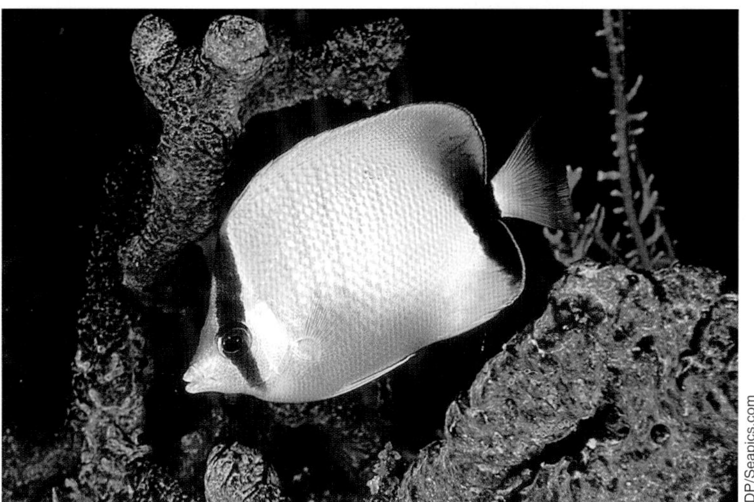

DP/Seapics.com

Above: **a reef butterflyfish.**

DP/Seapics.com

DP/Seapics.com

Angelfishes

(Family Pomacanthidae)

Related to butterflyfishes and somewhat resembling them, the angelfishes were included in the same family with butterflyfishes for many years. As in butterflyfishes, adult and juvenile angelfishes may differ strikingly in their markings and coloration. This trait makes juvenile angelfishes often hard to identify.

However, there are distinct differences between these two families. Angelfishes swim more gracefully, and many grow to a foot or more in length. Most angelfishes grow relatively long dorsal and anal fins, and their larval stage lacks the bony plates of the butterflyfishes. A conclusive difference is the angelfishes' large spine on the lower gill cover.

As a family, angelfishes feed on a variety of invertebrates, but some species are quite specialized feeders, eating primarily sponges. Others graze on algae. Still others eat a variety of soft-bodied invertebrates and even fish eggs.

Florida's cherubfish is an exception in the angelfish family, not exceeding three inches and lacking the long fins common to most angelfish species. The large, stunning queen angelfish may be the best-known of the family in Florida, and it is one of those species with distinctively different adult and juvenile color patterns. Other angelfish native to Florida include the black and yellow rock beauty, and the townsend angelfish, a natural hybrid between the queen angelfish and blue angelfish.

DP/Seapics.com

DP/Seapics.com

Top, left: **a queen angelfish.**

Top, right: **a gray angelfish.**

Left: **a juvenile queen angelfish.**

Bottom: **rock beauty angelfish**

DP/Seapics.com

BH/Seapics.com

DP/Seapics.com

Top: french angelfish.

Middle, left: a blue angelfish.

Middle, right: an intermediate phase of french angelfish.

DP/Seapics.com

DP/Seapics.com

Left: a diver with a blue angelfish.

Above: a French anglefish feeding on a sponge.

Sea Chubs

(Family Kyphosidae)

The chubs, or rudderfishes, are schooling reef fishes seldom seen in spite of being found inshore as well as offshore. They grow larger than two feet. Their incisor-like teeth lend themselves to the omnivorous diet of most of this family. Of the 42 species recognized, only two are common in Florida's coastal waters.

The Bermuda chub swims rapidly over reefs and along jetties and feeds primarily on macroalgae. Sometimes venturing into sea grass beds, it is found along both coasts and the Keys. The yellow chub occurs in the same areas as the Bermuda chub and displays many of the same behaviors. Both species often mix in the same school, and the two are very difficult to distinguish.

MU/Seapics.com

Top: **a school of Bermuda or yellow chub.**

Hawkfishes

(Family Cirrhitidae)

This small family inhabits tropical and subtropical reefs worldwide. Hawkfishes are small, colorful fishes recognized by lower pectoral fins which have separate rays, similar to scorpionfishes. A tuft of filaments, or cirri, tops each dorsal fin spine. Hawkfishes were named for their hawk-like hunting tactics. They feed on small fishes and crustaceans. Reminiscent of hawks, a hawkfish perches on its pectoral fins on a high point of the reef. When prey is spotted, the hawkfish swoops down and devours it.

Of the 32 family species, only one is known from Florida's waters. The secretive redspotted hawkfish likes coral and rocky reefs down to about 80 feet and may not be rare, but just hard to find.

DP/Seapics.com

Bottom: **a red-spotted hawkfish.**

IT'S AMOUR—SORT OF

Spawning in hawkfishes would be almost romantic if they didn't live in harems. These fish are protogynous hermaphrodites, beginning life as females. As they mature, the most dominant fish becomes a functional male, resulting in only a few dominant males in the population. The harem spreads over a specific territory where they perch on coral branches. During the day, most thoughts may be of food and shelter, but when the light dims, the young male hawkfish visits each female in his harem, looking for those ready to court. When he finds a suitable one, they swim upward off the reef in an arch, releasing sperm and eggs. The fertilized eggs drift away to become part of the plankton, and the hawkfishes settle back to the reef.

Cichlids

(Family Cichlidae)

No freshwater cichlid is native to Florida, but several introduced cichlids now call Florida home. Estimates of the number of cichlid species range from 900 to over 2000, almost exclusively from South and Central America and Africa. Their numbers would almost guarantee great diversity among the species, as well as numerous unifying similarities. Body shape is one of those diverse features. The angelfish from South America has a deep, compressed body with unusually high fins. A long, streamlined body is characteristic of the piscivores (fish-eating predators) in this family.

Feeding habits differ greatly, too. Some species eat microorganisms and algae they trap in mucus in their mouths and rake back to their throats where long, slender teeth are located. Other species prey on fishes, possibly even their own species, and their knife-like teeth slice up this meaty food for swallowing. Still other species eat mollusks, and their large, molar-like teeth grind the hard-shelled prey. A few species primarily graze on algae and aquatic plants. Such variety in this family allows it to utilize almost every niche where cichlids are found, making this family extremely successful, even in some difficult habitats.

In most cichlids, spawning involves an elaborate courtship display by the male. Usually his color intensifies, and he flares his fins, among a variety of body postures. In some species, particularly in Africa's Lake Malawi, males build large spawning sites on the sandy bottom. Some may be deep pits more than ten feet in diameter, while others may be mounds, like sandcastles, over three feet high. In both cases, nests are made by single fish that may not reach six inches in length. Several cichlids are mouth brooders. Others attach their eggs to rocks. Most, if not all, cichlids provide some degree of parental care for the eggs and young.

Around 20 cichlid species are established in Florida. A few are quite localized, such as the nile tilapia that seems to be confined to Lake Seminole. Others are more widespread.

The blue tilapia was introduced by the state government in the 1960s for aquatic weed control and sport fishing and hailed as a superfish. It proved a failure at both tasks but appreciated its new home so much it quickly spread to at least 18 counties. It is abundant in the St. Johns River. This mouth brooder supports a small commercial fishery in a few lakes in Florida.

The oscar apparently was released into canals from a fish farm near Miami in the 1950s. Its spread into much of southern Florida is believed to have been both natural and "helped" by anglers wanting to stock new waters.

Other cichlids enjoying their new home include the Rio Grande cichlid, the only cichlid native to the US (Texas); peacock cichlid, introduced into extreme southern Florida as a sport fish; and the black acara, which may spawn every month.

DP/Seapics.com

Top: **a blue tilapia.**
Below: a **Rio Grande cichlid.**
Bottom, left: **an oscar.**
Bottom, right: **a red oscar.**

VU - PC

VU

VU -BK

MS/Seapics.com

Damselfishes

(Family Pomacentridae)

The Pomacentridae is a large family of predominately small fishes. It may be the most conspicuous family on a coral reef in some regions. This family inhabits almost all tropical and warm temperate seas.

The habitat zones damselfish occupy are rather narrowly defined according to depth and type of bottom. Some species are found in shallow areas of vigorous wave action and little cover. Others live at greater depths among living or dead corals. Still others prefer sheltered lagoons. Some species are not tied exclusively to the reef itself but occupy mid-water depths above it. However, even these species usually retreat to the reef when danger threatens. Most damselfishes live at depths of six to 50 feet, but some go to depths of more than 300 feet. Diet varies in the family, but includes algae, plankton, and tiny, bottom-dwelling invertebrates. A

DP/Seapics.com

MS/Seapics.com

Top, left: **a juvenile yellowtail damselfish.**

Top, right: **a juvenile cocoa damselfish.**

Bottom: **a bicolor damselfish.**

few damselfishes eat coral polyps.

The interesting reproduction biology of damselfish has endeared them to many researchers. The bottom-dwelling damselfishes occupy well-defined territories they aggressively defend. A few days before spawning, the male cleans a rocky surface of algae and invertebrates growing on it. During all this nest preparation, he also finds time to "display" to females nearby. He really gets into his routine, too. His repertoire includes rapid swimming bursts, chasing the female, nipping her, and hovering with his fins fully extended. As spawning draws near, he may add rapid up and down swimming movements. Eventually, a receptive female leads her Romeo across the surface of the nest leaving a trail of eggs that stick to the rock, and her mate follows closely, fertilizing the eggs as he goes. In some species, several females will spawn with the same male in one nest. The male takes on most of the responsibility of caring for the nest and eggs. He fans the nest with his pectoral fins and removes dead eggs with his mouth. In two to seven days, the eggs hatch into almost transparent fry, and parental duties end at this point in most species. The fry drift with the plankton until they are carried to shallow reefs. There they settle to the bottom and take on their juvenile colors, often striking, and usually differing remarkably from drab, adult coloration.

Of the 321 species of Pomacentrids worldwide, perhaps 14 live in Florida. The common cocoa damselfish is found on the shallow reefs of South Florida and the Gulf.

DP/Seapics.com

DP/Seapics.com

DP/Seapics.com

DP/Seapics.com

Top, left: **a beaugregory (juvenile). This fish is fairly common in Florida. It inhabits areas of sand, sea-grasses, and coral rubble.**

Top, right: **a bicolor damselfish.**

Above: **a male sergeant major grooming red egg patch.**

Left: **a threespot damselfish (juvenile).**

DP/Seapics.com

Wrasses

(Family Labridae)

Wrasses are prolific, usually brightly-colored fishes, with prominent front teeth that make them look almost bucktoothed. Such teeth enable them to crush shells and exoskeletons of the mollusks and crustaceans that make up the bulk of the diet of most wrasses. The name, Labridae, was derived from the Greek "labros," which means "greedy." That accurately describes their feeding manners. The Labridae also range far and wide, from tropical to sub-Arctic regions as far north as Norway, and vary in size from a few inches to a few feet.

Wrasses of the genus *Labroides* are famous as cleaner fish. These fishes often take up stations on the reef where they wait for a larger fish to come to be cleaned. The cleaner wrasse boldly scours the body, fins, and mouth of "customers," removing parasites, mucus, and scales. Other wrasses sometimes follow larger fishes feeding along the bottom and eat the small invertebrates that are uncovered.

Most wrasses pass through several phases as they mature. In general, these changes in color and markings follow a pattern of juvenile phase (immature fish), initial phase (young adults of both sexes and older females), and terminal phase (mature males). Those in the terminal phase usually dominate spawning activity. These phases are so distinct scientists once thought individuals in different phases were separate species.

Over 400 species of wrasses have been described. Eighteen or so species occur in Florida. The largest, the hogfish, grows to three feet and sports impressively long dorsal spines. The pearly razorfish uses its blunt, razor-like head to dive into the sand when alarmed and "swims" in the sand using rapid body vibrations. The small yellowhead wrasse makes a spectacular sight in all its phases and reaches depths to 200 feet.

MK/Seapics.com

MStrickland/Seapics.com

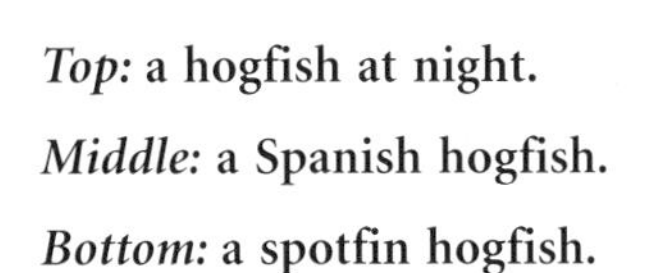

Top: **a hogfish at night.**

Middle: **a Spanish hogfish.**

Bottom: **a spotfin hogfish.**

Opposite page:

Top: **blueheaded wrasses feeding on eggs of sergeant major. Supermale below, initial phase above.**

Center, right: **a green razorfish.**

DP/Seapics.com

MK/Seapics.com

SEX CHANGE IN WRASSES AND PARROTFISHES--SUPERMALES

The abundance of wrasses around the world makes it clear they know what they are doing when it comes to reproduction. However, what wrasses find so easy, non-wrasse observers find hard to follow. It goes something like this.

Like many reef fishes, wrasses go through a sex reversal. Such a change isn't as uncommon as once thought. However, in wrasses and parrotfishes this change is spectacular. One individual is capable of being either male or female. Each sex displays different color patterns. It doesn't stop there, though. Wrasses also pass through different color phases as they mature. Immature fish display the juvenile phase of coloration, or JP. This phase is often quite striking. As they reach the young adult stage, they enter the initial phase of coloration (IP). Usually IP coloration is rather drab, but with some notable exceptions, such as the yellowhead wrasse. Most fishes in IP are female, but in a few species, some individuals in this phase are male. Such males are called "primary males" and may be indistinguishable from females. In time, some individuals in the IP change color and take on the terminal phase (TP). Females entering the TP change sex, as well as color, while primary males just change color. TP males are sometimes referred to as "supermales."

Terminal phase males are also usually dominant males and may establish either harems or temporary spawning territories. In most cases, spawning involves the TP male and one IP female. Not to be outdone, however, primary males (in the IP) often try to sneak into the spawning site disguised, so to speak, as a female. The interloper will then follow a pair of spawning fish and, at the pair's moment of spawning, will release his own milt into the water.

Naturally, not all wrasses follow the same strategy. That would be too easy. In some species, TP and IP fish engage in mass spawning. Some species have no primary males. In other species, the dominant male's aggression prevents females in his harem from changing to males. In the event this TP male is lost, the dominant female will take over the aggressive male role within a few hours, and a complete change to a functional male will occur within a few days.

Whoever said, "Variety is the spice of life," must have been thinking like a wrasse.

CLEANING STATIONS

A remarkable relationship exists between numerous reef fishes that satisfies one fish's need to be free of parasites and the other's need for food. Such relationships help both parties.

Several species of marine fishes and invertebrates pick parasites, scales, mucus, and dead tissue from the bodies of other, usually much larger fishes. Sometimes these cleaners even enter the larger fish's mouth to clean around its teeth. The larger fishes don't seem to eat their cleaners and may actually defend the small cleaners, at times.

On Florida's reefs, several species of neon gobies, juvenile spotfin hogfish, Spanish hogfish, and bluehead wrasses frequently set up cleaning stations. Some species of cleaners work alone or in pairs. Others clean their "customers" in small groups. Often cleaner fish establish more-or-less permanent stations on a reef where they wait for fishes wanting to be cleaned. Many of these cleaners wear bright colors that seem to advertise their cleaning stations. Sometimes fish line up to wait their turn. Apparently, groupers show up at these cleaning stations more often than other fishes. When ready to be cleaned, the customer fish signals its desire by opening its mouth, flaring its gills, and spreading its fins. The cleaner fish then scours the larger fish's body, including inside the mouth and gills. Throughout the cleaning, the larger fish remains nearly motionless. When the customer fish is satisfied about its cleaning, it shakes its body, and the cleaners swim away.

Some external parasites are nothing more than tiny crustaceans living between the fish's scales and feeding on the fish's tissue. Such parasitism may not cause the host fish any real harm. Still, the plucky little predators pick these tiny crustaceans from between the fish's scales and occasionally pick off a scale as well.

DP/Seapics.com

Top: **sharknose gobies and a shrimp clean parasites from a tiger grouper.**

Parrotfishes

(Family Scaridae)

Like the avian parrots, parrotfishes possess powerful jaws, teeth fused into beaks, and usually bright coloration. Some parrotfishes go it alone, while others form loose groups. As a group, parrotfishes take a variety of food items, including algae, sponges, coral polyps, and sea urchins. Most parrotfishes inhabit reefs, often in large numbers. Only a very few species venture into sea-grass beds.

Parrotfishes share with wrasses the spectacular changes in sex and color involved with maturation. Terminal phase males spawn with individual females, and the other males and females engage in mass spawning.

Active only during day, parrotfishes settle for the night into reef crevices. Several species also secrete an envelope of mucus around themselves. The envelope is open at both ends, allowing water to flow past the sleeping fish. Since this mucus envelope is foul-tasting, perhaps it offers a measure of protection against nighttime predators.

DP/Seapics.com

Right: **a rainbow parrotfish asleep at night. Note the powerful jaws with the teeth fused into a beak-like structure.**

DP/Seapics.com

DP/Seapics.com

Top: **a stoplight parrotfish supermale. Adult males in certain species of parrotfishes and the closely related wrasses may come in two forms, males and "supermales," which may be so radically different in appearance that in the past they would have been considered different species. "Regular" males may more closely resemble females, but both are reproductively fully funcional. The precise reasons for this phenomenon are still not well understood.**

Left: **a midnight parrotfish.**

MR. SANDMAN

Parrotfishes can do something few, if any, other fishes can do: make sand. These chewing machines possess a second set of jaws in their throats (pharyngeal jaws) with rows of teeth that process the parrotfishes' food. Parrotfishes graze on algae that cover the coral and sometimes eat the coral polyps, as well as other encrusting organisms. In the process, they ingest sizable quantities of coral. Their pharyngeal teeth grind all ingested material into paste. The food particles are digested, and coral particles are excreted as fine limestone sand. Schooling parrotfishes may release clouds of chalky residue as they feed across the reef, their crunching often audible to divers. Thus, simply by eating, parrotfishes have become a major source of sediment on reefs.

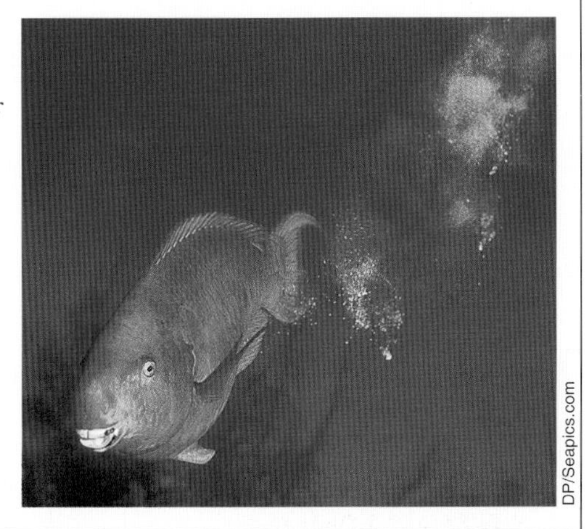

DP/Seapics.com

Right: **a blue parrotfish terminal male releases a cloud of sand in its excrement.**

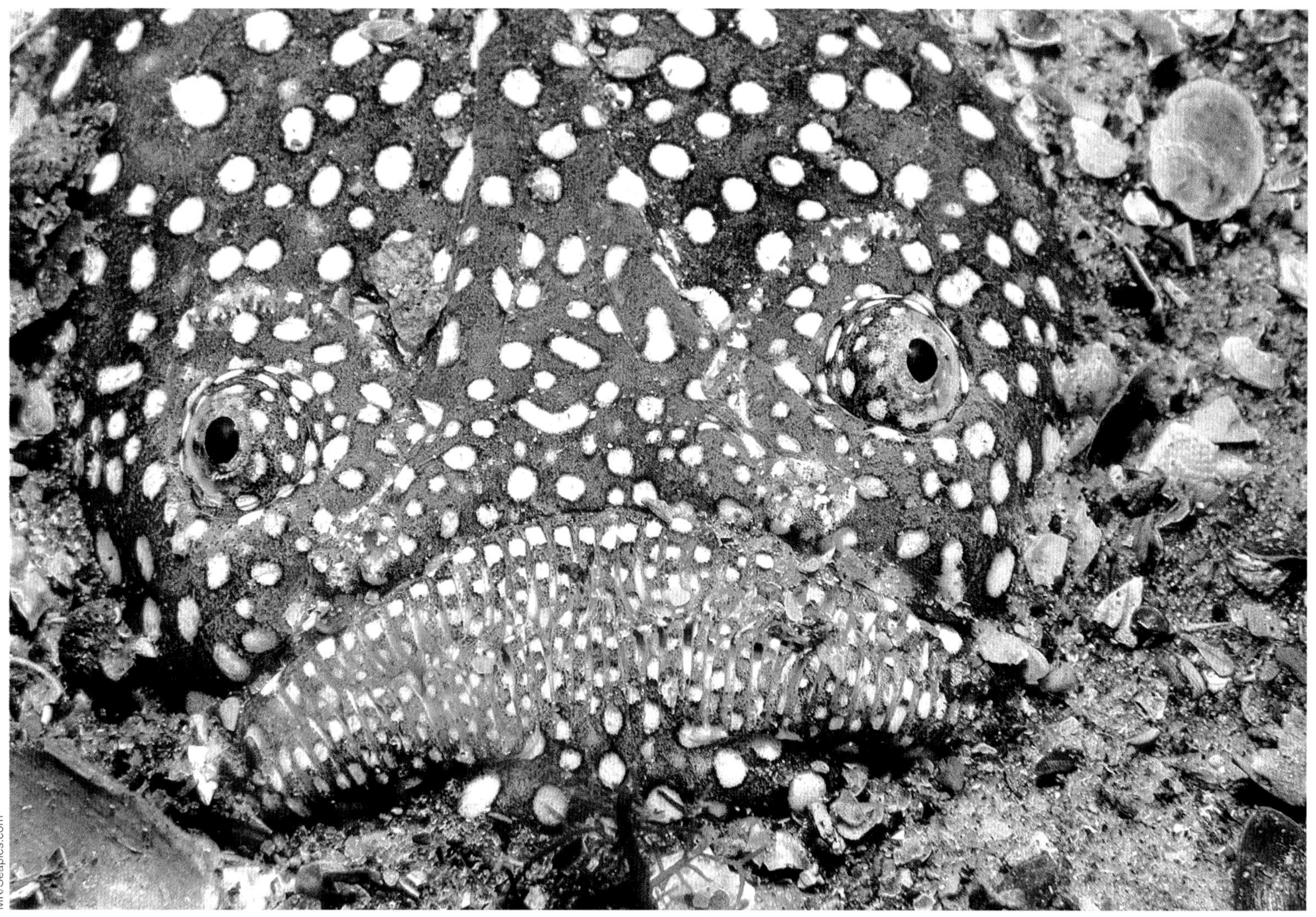

Stargazers

(Family Uranoscopidae)

Look at a bulldog head-on to get a good idea of what a stargazer looks like from the same perspective. These small fish burrow into sand, leaving only eyes and lips exposed. That's not hard for them to do since their small eyes sit squarely on top of their heads, hence their common name, "stargazer." From this position, stargazers can ambush the small fishes and invertebrates on which they feed. This family can deliver an uncomfortable electrical shock from special organs associated with the eye muscles. For a little added punch, stargazers also possess a poison gland associated with a spine on the shoulder girdle above the pectoral fin. Handle with care—or better yet, don't handle.

Approximately 50 species of stargazers are recognized around the world. Perhaps four species of these secretive fish live in Florida's vicinity, but only one lives in shallow water. The southern stargazer has bones on the top of its head that form a Y, hence the species name, *y-graecum.* This stargazer may be found in soft-bottom areas of Florida's inshore waters. The lancer stargazer lives in the deeper waters of the middle and outer shelf.

Top and bottom: **stargazers.**

Triplefins

(Family Tripterygiidae)

This family of small blenny-like fish was named for the three distinct sections of dorsal fins. The first two sections possess only spines, while the third possesses only soft rays. This family is represented around the world except, apparently, for the Atlantic coasts of Africa and South America. The majority of triplefins live on reefs. The rather cryptic coloration of most triplefins allows them to blend rather well with algae and coral branches on reef's, making them difficult to observe. These bottom-dwellers feed on small invertebrates.

This family includes about 115 species, with perhaps three species occurring around Florida's southern coastline. The redeye triplefin is more common in the Bahamas than Florida and lives on coral reefs to a depth of about 35 feet. The roughhead triplefin is found occasionally on reefs of southeastern Florida.

Top: **a redeye triplefin.**

MU/Seapics.com

Sand Stargazers

(Family Dactyloscopidae)

The small sand stargazers, compared to stargazers, have three ventral fin rays instead of the stargazers' five and have more slender and rounded bodies, in contrast to the stargazers' square-shaped bodies. They do have similar habits. Both hide in the sand with their eyes exposed and ambush prey. Sand stargazers are found in warm marine waters of the western hemisphere, where they often associate with reefs, burrowing into sand, leaving only their eyes exposed. Many species have peculiar tubular eyes. Males of some species carry a clump of eggs beneath each of their rather large pectoral fins. Eight species occur in Florida.

Clingfishes

(Family Gobiesocidae)

Some people say clingfishes look like tadpoles. Others pinned this family with the name "skilletfish," referring to their large, flat heads, and slender bodies. Clingfishes are mostly small, inshore species, widely distributed throughout temperate and some tropical seas. Most sit on the bottom, but some cling to seaweed or sea-grasses, and a few deeper water species attach themselves to sponges. A clingfish's most distinctive feature may be the sucker on its breast used to attach the fish to rocks in the wave zone and sometimes to plants. The only clingfish common in Florida's inshore waters is the skilletfish, which is especially partial to oyster reefs, where it often lays eggs in empty oyster shells.

Wormfishes and Dartfishes

(Family Microdesmidae)

The Microdesmidae is believed to be closely related to the gobies, and like gobies, lacks a lateral line. Dartfishes actually resemble gobies a bit more than wormfishes since dartfishes have two separate dorsal fins, and wormfishes have a single continuous dorsal fin. Wormfishes are peculiar, nocturnal fishes that burrow in rubble and sediment around reefs. Several species are known to eat planktonic crustaceans, such as copepods.

There are about 60 members of this family, but very few from Florida waters. They seem to be rare fish, but that may be as much because they are seldom seen or are confused with other fish. The pink wormfish can be expected in many areas of quiet, shallow water around the state but is considered especially rare in the northern Gulf. The pugjaw wormfish is found in the coastal areas and coral reefs of southeastern Florida and the Keys to depths of about 100 feet, but may be more common in shallow water over reef flats.

MK/Seapics.com

Above: **blue dartfish.**

Blennies

(Suborder Blennioidei)

"Blenny" is a name commonly applied to several families of closely related, predominantly marine fishes. Blennies share certain characteristics. All blennies are small. Their pelvic fins consist of only a tiny hidden, or embedded, spine and two to four soft rays. The long dorsal fin extends from the head almost to the tail, or even joining the tail in some species. Many blennies have cirri (thin, fleshy filaments) on their nostrils, eyes, or neck. Most have relatively large eyes, small mouths, and feed primarily on benthic invertebrates.

Most blennies are secretive and cryptically colored, shallow reef dwellers. In some species, males and females appear quite different. Several species are spectacularly colored.

Blennies have strong pectoral fins which can be used to push the fish across rocks if it becomes stranded in tidal pools.

Top: **a wrasse blenny.**

Middle, right: **a hairy blenny.**

Middle, left: **a redlip blenny.**

Bottom, left: **a saddled blenny.**

Bottom, right: **a rosy blenny.**

DP/Seapics.com

MU/Seapics.com

DP/Seapics.com

MPO/Seapics.com

MU/Seapics.com

MK/Seapics.com

LABRISOMIDS

Labrisomids are set apart from other blennies by having fixed, conical teeth. This family of over 100 species occurs primarily in the warm seas of the western hemisphere, with only a few species present along the coasts of Africa and parts of northern Asia. Interestingly, the eastern Pacific species of the genus Starksia *are livebearers, while the western Atlantic species of the same genus apparently are not. This family includes some of the largest of the blennies.*

*There are 19 labrisomid blennies in Florida waters. The two-inch checkered blenny inhabits rocky and coral reefs and is often found inside tube sponges. Males of this genus (*starskia, *to which the checkered blenny belongs) have a copulatory organ formed from the free anal fin spines. The hairy blenny is a common blenny of the reef tops, often found in quite shallow water, and is Florida's largest blenny, at seven to eight inches. Other labrisomids in Florida include the rosy blenny, found in shallow sponge and sea-grass beds, and the key blenny, which lives in the Keys.*

MK/Seapics.com

Top: **a seaweed blenny peering out from an encrusted bottle.**

Right: **a tesselated blenny peers out from empty barnacle shells on an oil rig in the Gulf of Mexico. The fish posing in a vertical position is a seaweed blenny.**

Pikeblennies, Tubeblennies, and Flagblennies

(Family Chaenopsidae)

This tropical family of small blennies usually sports cirri above the eye, on the nostrils, and on the side of the nape (dorsal surface just behind the head). Most species live in holes, abandoned worm tubes in the sand, or coral rubble, and feed on small crustaceans. A few species eat small fishes.

When the courting urge strikes males of many species, they begin a rhythmic jerking in and out of their holes, erecting their fins to attract a mate.

Of the 56 species in this family, about 13 species are found in Florida's waters. Sailfin blennies are found near the coast in southern Florida and the Gulf, living in holes among the coral rubble in sandy areas. Males emerge from their holes in the morning and afternoon and rapidly raise and lower their dorsal and anal fins in an ardent display.

Other species known in Florida include the bluethroat pikeblenny which prefers worm tubes in sea-grass beds and sandy areas in very shallow water, and the rare banner blenny, first discovered in the stomach of a snapper.

MK/Seapics.com

Top: **a bluethroat pikeblenny.**

DP/Seapics.com

Above: **a Molly Miller.**

MIMICRY IN BLENNIES

Someone once noted that imitation is the sincerest form of flattery. Several blennies go well beyond imitation. Blennies aren't the only fishes known to mimic others, but some blennies excel. Most often, the mimic blennies are those that feed by nipping the bodies of other fishes. Mimicry in these species doesn't stop at being similar. It copies both physical traits (body shape and color) and behavioral traits (such as swimming patterns). Some blennies mimic wrasses, no small feat since blennies are known for their jerky movements and wrasses for their smooth style.

The blenny enjoys certain benefits from its flattery. Many wrasses are accepted by other fishes as cleaner fish. Mimicry in this case allows the blenny the opportunity to move in on its unsuspecting victim. What a surprise it must be for a fish expecting the removal of a parasite to get a painful nip removing part of itself instead. Also, most wrasses aren't fish-eating. In this case a blenny might be able to approach smaller fish unconcerned about a harmless "wrasse." The heads of small fishes have been found in the stomachs of some blennies, suggesting this tactic works.

Not all mimic blennies mimic other fish; some mimic other blennies. Can there be a benefit for one blenny to mimic another blenny? Some blennies have well-developed venom glands, and the means to deliver venom, along with a painful bite. If predatory fishes grab one of these blennies, they usually spit it back out alive—quickly. Presumably, the blenny inflicted a painful nip on the inside of the larger fish's mouth. Studies suggest that predators that have experienced such a distasteful blenny meal, don't go back for more. Other blennies that mimic one of these fanged blennies receive a measure of protection from predatory fishes with the "blenny experience." Apparently, "once stung, twice shy."

Combtooth Blennies

(Family Blenniidae)

"Combtooth" comes from the single row of closely set, incisor-like teeth in each jaw. Most combtooth blennies have cirri on the eyes, and some species also have cirri on the nostrils and nape. Blennies are marine species in our area. Most blennies lack swim bladders and are confined to a life on the bottom.

Blennies are active during the day. As with many benthic fishes, blennies establish territories. Some blennies in this family feed on plankton, while others scrape algae and small invertebrates off encrusted rocks and coral. Still others dart out of their holes to nip fins and skin of other fish. These employ a pair of canine-like teeth to remove bits of skin, scales, or mucus, on which they feed.

Male blennies build nest caves, visited by females that may leave and reenter several times. The eggs adhere to cave walls, and the male fans his fins over them, expelling sperm. He then guards the nest until the eggs hatch.

Among the 345 species in this family around the world (with 17 species in Florida), Florida has the namesake Florida blenny. This three-inch blenny occurs primarily on grass flats and oyster beds along much of both coasts. Multiple females may mate with the same male in a single day. Several other blennies in Florida include the mostly herbivorous Molly Miller, commonly found around jetties in western Florida.

MK/Seapics.com

Dragonets

(Family Callionymidae)

Dragonets live on the bottom in marine habitats. Some species bury themselves in the sand by day, while others dart from rock to rock looking for food. In most species, males can be distinguished by their longer dorsal spines and tail fin rays, as well as by more brilliant coloration. Dragonets consume a variety of benthic invertebrates living among the rubble most of the family call home.

About 130 species of dragonets occur worldwide. In Florida, the most commonly encountered is the lancer dragonet, found on sand close to shallow reefs down to a depth of 300 feet. The spotfin dragonet is seen much less frequently since it lives around reefs much deeper than 300 feet.

Top: **a lancer dragonet. Some species of dragonets are colorful fish found around Indo-Pacific reefs and some are so spectacular that they are featured in the aquarium trade. The six species found in Florida are less colorful.**

Sleepers

(Family Eleotridae)

The sleepers tolerate a wide range of salinity, but most often are found in lower salinity waters near the coast. Some species enter freshwater habitats.

Sleepers may have received their common name from their eyes, which tend to have a "glassy" look, much like that of a high school algebra student. Called gudgeons or bullies in some regions, sleepers occur primarily in tropical and subtropical waters, rarely in temperate areas. They tend to be secretive animals but may be seen sometimes on bottom in a position that looks as if they are standing on their forward fins. Sleepers prey on a variety of benthic invertebrates and small fishes.

Of the approximately 150 species of sleepers, six occur along Florida's coast. The fat sleeper is found in estuaries around the state and ventures into fresh water, at times. This species is one of the more conspicuous members of this shy family. The bigmouth sleeper is one of the largest of the family, at 24 inches, and is found in the estuaries along South Florida's coast.

VU - FR

VU - RJG

Above: **a fat sleeper (juvenile).**

Bottom: **a bigmouth sleeper.**

DP/Seapics.com

THE LIFE CYCLE OF GOBIES

It is believed most gobies follow a similar life cycle. The female lays from just a few to several hundred eggs, attaching them to vegetation, shells, or rocks. The male then fertilizes the eggs and remains to guard them after the female departs. The eggs hatch into small transparent larvae that are dispersed by currents. Usually in a matter of days, the larvae settle to the bottom and quickly change coloration to match their new environment. The young of freshwater gobies are carried downstream and out to sea where they spend their early larval period. Gobies grow rather quickly, and in warm water may mature in only a few months. Cooler water gobies need a year or two to mature. In recent years, researches have discovered that a few species of gobies change sex, male to female, though most species probably do not.

Gobies

(Family Gobiidae)

Gobies belong to one of the largest fish families, with more species than any other tropical family. They also occur very commonly in certain habitats and exhibit great diversity. Gobies like privacy and tend to hide. Most species are cryptically colored.

In general, gobies are small, bottom-dwelling fishes that have two dorsal fins and a sucking disc fused from the paired pelvic fins. The smallest vertebrates in the world are gobies of the genus *Trimmatom*. Gobies also lack the sensory lateral line down their sides possessed by most fishes. Plenty of exceptions exist in this large family, however. For instance, the violet goby, found in tidal creeks and canals along Florida's coasts, grows up to 19 inches long. The peppermint goby, of the Florida Keys, has pelvic fins which are almost separate. There are other exceptions, as well.

Gobies occur around the world, except in the Arctic and Antarctic oceans. The family ranges through various habitats, from marine coral reefs to estuaries and muddy bays, and from sandy beaches to the continental shelf. Some species occur in fresh water, and most gobies are tropical species. Though the majority of gobies stay on the bottom, some species swim freely and may form schools. Many of these free swimmers feed on plankton. Other species eat primarily small invertebrates; some eat small fishes; a few eat mostly algae.

No one knows for sure how many different species of gobies exist around the world. Estimates range to over 2000 species. If true, that would make one out every ten species of fish a goby. The waters around Florida contain 23 genera of gobies and 58 species. The six-inch frillfin goby inhabits tide pools and rocky shallows to a depth of about ten feet. Named for its free upper pectoral fin rays, this energetic little goby has been seen jumping from one tide pool to another. During a study of the neon goby, a native of southeastern Florida and the Keys, researchers noted that one pair spawned nine times in two weeks.

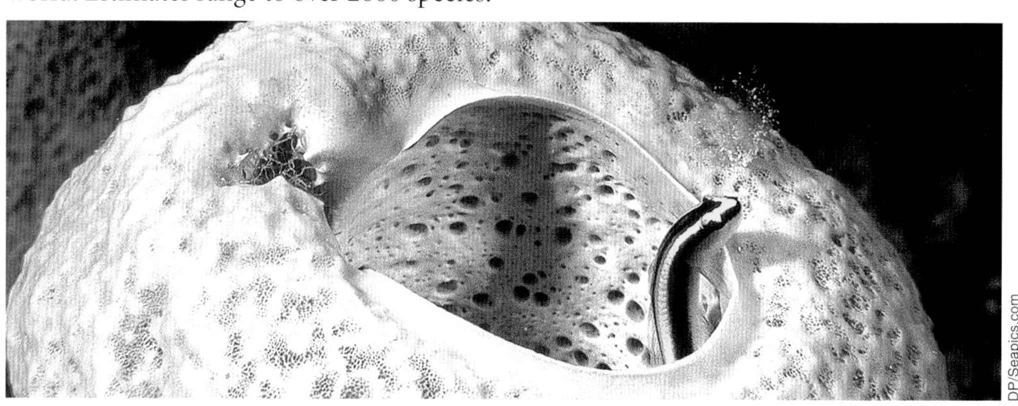

DP/Seapics.com

MK/Seapics.com

Top:* a peppermint goby perched on star coral.

Middle:* a sharknose goby hides in the excurrent pore of a purple tube sponge from which water is expelled.

Bottom:* an orangespotted goby shares a burrow with a nearly blind alpheid shrimp. The shrimp digs and maintains the burrow while the goby watches for predators.

MU/Seapics.com

MU/Seapics.com

MK/Seapics.com

LIFE TOGETHER

In a large family, a variety of unusual lifestyles is expected, and gobies have come up with some of the best. One of the more interesting is a symbiotic relationship many gobies have with marine invertebrates. To be truly symbiotic, the relationship must benefit both parties. In most cases, the benefit to the goby is its home, which it shares with the nice home builder, often a burrowing shrimp or crab. In return, the goby provides sentry duty. Prawn-gobies, for example, live in the burrows of blind (or nearly blind) prawns. The prawn keeps the burrow cleaned out, and the goby acts as a lookout. Such cooperation enables both parties to survive when it would have been much more difficult alone.

On coral reefs, gobies often associate with snapping shrimps. Usually in pairs, the shrimp construct a zigzag network of tunnels in the sand. Snapping shrimp have a large claw they use much like a spade to carry sand from inside their burrow to dump a short distance away from the entrance. Out of its burrow, the shrimp is quite vulnerable. The goby sits outside the entrance to the burrow keeping watch. When the shrimp is ready to come out, it touches the goby's tail with one of its antennae. If the coast is clear, the goby wiggles its tail a certain way, and the shrimp ventures out to dump its load of sand. If the goby sees a predator lurking about, it doesn't give the all clear signal. If things get too tense, the goby dives into the hole. In return, the goby gets to eat the worms and small tidbits found in the sand which the shrimp excavates from its burrow.

Other associations aren't so clear. Some gobies live in or closely around corals, sponges, or similar invertebrates. Many of these gobies feed on plankton. The fish gain a hiding place and can move higher to a zone richer in plankton. In most cases, one male will dwell with two or more females in the same clump of coral or sponge. If the male dies, there is no need to mourn. One of the females conveniently changes to a male. It is not known what benefits the coral or the sponge receives from this relationship.

***Top:* a neon goby on brain coral.**

***Center:* a bridled goby.**

Left: dash gobies at their burrow opening.

MU/Seapics.com

Spadefishes

(Family Ephippidae)

Spadefishes are common in many coastal areas of the western Atlantic and Gulf. Spadefishes resemble angelfishes, but spadefishes have deeply notched dorsal fins, while angelfishes have a continuous dorsal fin. Spadefishes also lack the angelfishes' spine on the gill cover. The family contains 23 species, but only one is found in Florida.

The Atlantic spadefish is common around reefs, sea walls, bridge pilings, and similar barnacle-encrusted structures where invertebrates make up the bulk of its diet.

Very small spadefish are round, dark, and inhabit estuaries where they often float on the surface, looking very much like fallen leaves. Older juveniles develop the prominent dark bars associated with spadefish. As they reach maturity, the bars tend to disappear. Adults often form fairly large schools. Like sheepshead, spadefish frequently fall victim to sudden cold snaps in the shallow waters along the coast.

VU - JB

Top and right: **Atlantic spadefish.**

DP/Seapics.com

Surgeonfishes

(Family Acanthuridae)

Surgeonfishes are among the most conspicuous fishes on tropical reefs. By day, divers often see schools of surgeonfishes grazing across the reef.

This family's common name refers to the very sharp, scalpel-like spines located on each side of the base of the tail. Some Indo-Pacific and eastern Pacific species have fixed spines or rigid plates, but Atlantic species possess movable spines. When the fish flexes its body, the spines stand out at about a 45° angle, enough to inflict deep slashes when the fish flips its tail. These spines are highly modified scales. In the Florida species, the spines are not easily noticeable, but are very obvious on certain Pacific species.

DP/Seapics.com

DP/Seapics.com

Most of the 70 or so species of surgeonfishes are largely herbivorous, using small, serrate, incisor-like teeth to nip algae from rocks and corals. Often, tiny invertebrates associated with the algae are eaten, too.

BH/Seapics.com

Only three species of surgeonfish are native to Florida, and all are similar in adult size, 13 to 14 inches. The blue tang has the most distinctive coloration of Florida's surgeonfish. The young usually are bright yellow; the adults bright blue. The ocean surgeon is found in shallow, hard-bottom areas along both Florida coasts. The doctorfish often travels in schools with the ocean surgeonfish and frequently changes the intensity of the vertical bars on its sides. These bars distinguish the doctorfish from the other two surgeonfish species.

Top: **a school of blue tangs feeding in a bed of turtle grass.**

Center, left: **a blue tang juvenile.**

Center, right: **a blue tang adult.**

Bottom: **a doctorfish.**

Butterfishes

(Family Stromateidae)

The butterfishes join the milieu of controversial families involved with the driftfishes. These families just don't fit neatly in their boxes. Some species even resemble small jacks, except butterfishes lack pelvic fins.

Young butterfishes usually drift among plankton and often associate with jellyfish, similar to the driftfishes. These are open-water, schooling fishes that live near the bottom as adults, in some cases in quite deep water. They range along the coasts of North and South America, western Africa, and southern Asia, mostly over sandy bottoms fairly close to shore.

Of the 13 species in this family, only three occur in Florida's waters. The butterfish grows to about twelve inches and schools in inshore waters along Florida's coasts, sometimes entering estuaries. Juveniles feed on plankton, and adults feed largely on jellyfish. The Gulf butterfish occurs along Florida's West Coast but is more common near Louisiana. The harvestfish is a bit smaller than the other two, growing to only ten inches.

Driftfishes

(Family Nomeidae)

The driftfishes make up another family that has generated confusion on the part of those who classify animals. Formerly assigned to the same family as butterfishes (Stromateidae), and classified today by some scientists in the family Ariommatidae, driftfishes display characteristics that fit still another family, Centrolophidae (ruffs). Confusing matters even more, the name "driftfish" is used for members of different families. Such is the world of taxonomy.

This small family lives near the surface of open oceans in tropical and temperate regions and often associates with other animals, such as jellyfish, or even with seaweed. Apparently, jellyfish protect these usually small fishes and may even serve as a food source for some. The scales of driftfishes are weak and easily shed, which complicates identification. Often lateral line scale counts help to identify a fish, but this method is unreliable in any fish that loses scales easily. The nomeids also possess a network of mucus canals along the sides that may be visible through the skin. Of the 15 or so species, perhaps five or six occur along Florida's coast.

The man-of-war fish often associates with the Portuguese man-of-war and has been observed to nibble on the jellyfish's polyps. The jellyfish's tentacles protect the fish, which is immune to their toxin. The bigeye cigarfish breaks with this family's small tradition and grows to a length of 30 inches.

Gouramis

(Family Belontiidae)

At least one gourami has joined the long list of exotic fishes introduced into Florida. Gouramis come from the tropical and subtropical fresh waters of Asia and Africa. The various gouramis range in size from the one-inch licorice gourami to the appropriately named giant gourami at over three feet. The family is probably best known for its labyrinth, an auxiliary breathing organ formed of a convoluted network of tissue located near the gills. The lung-like labyrinth enables gouramis (and related fishes) to survive in poorly oxygenated water as long as they can reach the surface to breathe.

Another common feature in this family is their thread-like pectoral fins. Gouramis can move these fins independently of each other as sensory organs, exploring their immediate environment. Males in most species brood the eggs, either in their mouths, or in bubble nests they build at the surface.

The croaking gourami has been introduced into South Florida. This shy and peaceful, two-inch native of Southeast Asia has become established in canals within the Lake Worth Drainage area in Palm Beach County. The croaking gourami is a bubble-nest builder, and during courtship both mates may make loud grunting noises.

Cutlassfishes

(Family Trichiuridae)

This family has long, ribbon-like bodies and large, fang-like teeth. Most species occur in the deep waters of tropical and temperate seas. Only one species inhabits Florida's inshore waters and is likely to be seen with any regularity.

The Atlantic cutlassfish, or ribbonfish, is common in Florida bays in warmer months, but it also goes into deep waters of the continental shelf. This fish-eater can inflict a painful bite with its sharp teeth. In fact, its teeth have been found imbedded in seismic cable—perhaps deliberately bitten?

CIGUATERA FISH POISONING

Ciguatera poisoning is the most frequently reported seafood-related disease. It happens when a person eats fish that contain the toxin. Symptoms include headache and vertigo in the first two to twelve hours, followed by nausea, vomiting, a drop in blood pressure, and an irregular heart beat. Severe cases may also include paralysis, comatosis, and rarely death. Symptoms intensify after the consumption of alcoholic beverages.

Fish poisoning isn't new. The first known case was reported in the West Indies in 1555. Similar cases were noted during the Spanish explorations of the New World. Later, the ship's surgeon on H.M.S. Bounty (of Mutiny On The Bounty *fame) died in Tahiti from fish poisoning. Much more recently, three families in Canada contracted the disease in 1998 after eating barracuda imported to Montreal from Florida. Today, estimates of ciguatera poisoning range from 20,000 to 50,000 cases each year worldwide.*

It wasn't until the 1970s that a benthic dinoflagellate was identified as the primary producer of ciguatoxin. Gambierdiscus toxicus *is an epiphytic dinoflagellate widespread throughout the tropics in association with coral reefs. An epiphyte is a plant (in this case tiny algae) that attaches to another plant (in this case larger algae) for support but is not parasitic. The main areas for ciguatera are the Caribbean, Indian, and Pacific oceans. Cases reported in the US and Canada are usually attributed to tourism in affected areas or fish exports.*

Ciguatera toxin accumulates in ever increasing amounts as it is passed up the food chain. Herbivorous fishes, such as surgeonfish, graze on algae growing on the reef and ingest G. toxicus *in the process. At the top, large predatory fish, such as groupers, snappers, and barracudas consume the smaller fishes. With each step up the food ladder, the toxin accumulates in greater amounts. Large predators may accumulate enough toxin to affect people.*

Any coral reef fish can be affected, but barracudas are most often implicated in cases of fish poisoning. Currently no practical tests are available to determine which fish carry this toxin. Cooking and freezing don't inactivate the toxin, either.

DP/Seapics.com

Barracudas

(Family Sphyraenidae)

Barracudas, like many sharks, have a reputation for being dangerous. Their moderate to large size, knife-like teeth, and predatory nature suggest at least a potential risk, and a few confirmed reports of attacks on divers who were spear-fishing support that reputation. In reality, there may be a greater risk from eating barracudas than from being bitten by one—at least barracudas from the tropics. Tropical barracudas have earned a reputation for causing ciguatera poisoning (see box on opposite page). Those caught in temperate waters apparently don't cause such poisoning.

Barracudas' slender, arrow-shaped bodies are built for speed, helping to make these fish efficient, as well as voracious predators of other fishes. Locating prey with acute eyesight, barracudas charge prey at great speed and take large snapping bites with powerful jaws.

Twenty species are identified within the single genus of barracudas. Three or four of these are found in Florida.

The largest of these barracudas is the great barracuda, which may reach more than six feet long. These fish are found throughout Florida's coastal waters, ranging from inshore mangroves to open ocean, and often found over reefs. Their unnerving habit of following divers around reefs does nothing to improve their reputation, but this habit seems to be merely fishy curiosity. The great barracuda is most often seen alone or in small groups.

The guaguanche is the most common barracuda in the Gulf. This is a fish of open waters rather than reefs. It grows only to two feet, and it is caught frequently in shrimpers' trawls.

The sennet is uncommon in Florida.

DP/Seapics.com

***Top:* a great barracuda with a diver.**

***Right:* a diver feeding "tame" barracuda in front of underwater statue at Key Largo.**

***Below:* a close-up of the powerful jaws of the great barracuda.**

DP/Seapics.com

DW/Seapics.com

Top: **yellowfin tuna.**

Mackerels and Tunas

(Family Scombridae)

This family includes some of the world's best known fishes. Mackerels and tunas are widely distributed in tropical and temperate seas. Some of the 49 species live along the coast; others remain in the open sea.

These fishes have been called "swimming machines" because almost every external feature fits together remarkably in a design that maximizes hydrodynamic performance. Their streamlined bodies contain grooves into which different fins can be tucked to reduce turbulence and drag. The rigid tail, with its deeply forked fin, provides maximum thrust at high speeds. The red muscle that makes up a large proportion of the body is just the type of muscle needed to permit continuous activity. Tunas, in particular, can maintain a body temperature several degrees warmer than the water, allowing a higher metabolic rate, which provides the higher level of energy these fishes need for their continuous, high-speed swimming. In addition, these fishes can make bursts of very high speed. Wahoo, found infrequently in the open ocean all around Florida, can reach 47 miles per hour.

Scombrids are built to swim fast, and swim they must. Continuous swimming ventilates the gills. Some species simply can't pump enough water over their gills to meet their respiratory needs unless they keep swimming. Speed isn't the only feature of this family's swimming ability. They have great stamina, too. Tunas, for example, are known for their long-distance migrations. One study involving tagging and recapturing tuna, documented a tuna that traveled 4,774 miles across the Atlantic in 119 days.

Most tunas and mackerels travel in schools and live near the surface of open waters over the continental shelf or beyond, feeding on other fishes and squid.

The abundant Spanish mackerel schools in open water and often enters bays. The Atlantic bonito, or little tuna, enters shallower water than other tunas. It also is smaller, growing only to about two feet in length, in contrast to the offshore yellowfin tuna, which grows to more than six feet.

RH/Seapics.com

Above: **an albacore.**

JW/Seapics.com

Above: **a skipjack tuna or aku.**

DP/Seapics.com

Above: **a king mackerel or kingfish.**

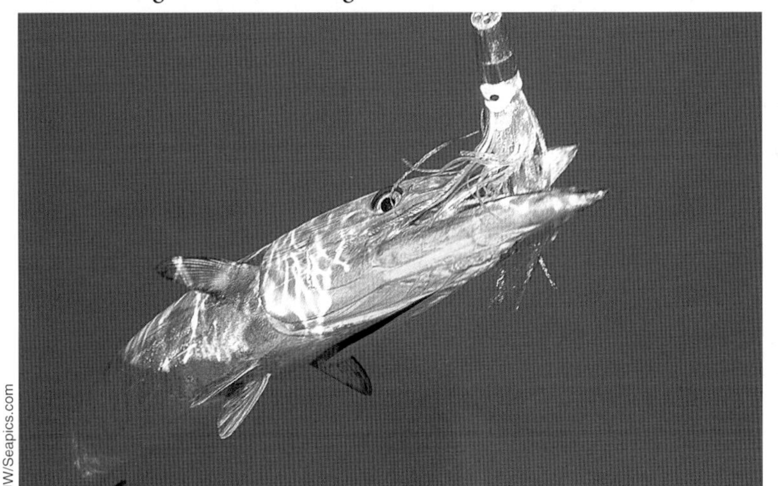
JW/Seapics.com

Above: **a wahoo (also called ono or Pacific kingfish).**

DP/Seapics.com

Above: **another wahoo.**

DP/Seapics.com

Above: **a cero mackerel.**

WARM-BLOODED FISH?

Almost all fishes are cold-blooded. Their body temperature is dictated by the temperature of the surrounding water. However, several fishes, including tunas, keep their bodies warm independent of water temperature, much after the fashion of better-recognized warm-blooded animals, such as mammals. This is no easy feat for a fish because their gills act much like the radiator of a car. Blood flows through the gills, picking up oxygen from the water as it goes. In this continuous process, the blood also transfers heat from the fish to the surrounding water. Unlike most fishes, tunas can block much of that transfer of heat, as well as generate body heat. A large central muscle in tunas generates heat, as does their high metabolic rate. A complex, counter-current circulation of blood keeps most body heat inside their bodies and away from the gills, where it would be lost quickly. In this way, tunas enter the ranks of other warm-blooded, or endothermic, animals.

FB/Seapics.com

Swordfish

(Family Xiphiidae)

When it comes to small families, this one ranks with the smallest: one genus, one species. The swordfish roams widely in open oceans throughout most of the world. In cooler waters, swordfish can be seen at the surface, but in the warmer waters of the Gulf, they stay deeper. In fact, swordfish range from the surface to depths of over 2000 feet. Swordfish are thought to spawn throughout the warm months in the Caribbean and Gulf of Mexico. Swordfish grow large, close to 1,200 pounds. The fishing pressure on swordfish and other "billfish" has raised the concern that the fish populations can't hold up over the long run.

Some scientists consider the Xiphiidae family to include the sailfish and spearfishes. However, the swordfish lacks scales and pelvic fins and has a flattened bill, or rostrum, rather than a round one.

Above: **a swordfish.**

Bottom: **another view of the swordfish. Note that the swordfish has no pelvic fins, whereas the billfish (on the following page) has small pelvic fins.**

GDS/Seapics.com

Top: a sailfish with dorsal fin down for speed.

Billfishes (marlins, spearfishes, and sailfishes)

(Family Istiophoridae)

This rather large family includes marlins, spearfishes, and sailfishes. All are large fishes and, like sharks, billfishes are recognized as apex predators, those at the top of the food chain. Though found worldwide, billfishes tend to stay in rather small, disjunct populations that are highly migratory. Billfishes (and swordfish) share with tunas and mackerels many features needed for rapid, continuous swimming. Like tunas, the billfishes are warm-blooded—at least, to a degree. In billfishes, the heat-generating muscle is near the eyes and warms only the brain and eyes.

Within this family it is likely that more species have been described than actually exist. Adding to this confusion is the relative dearth of information about the life histories of the billfishes. At least, scientists have determined that sailfish around the world belong to the same species, and some consider that Atlantic and Pacific populations of blue marlin to represent the same species.

The sailfish is instantly recognized by its exceptionally high dorsal fin. Sailfish grow fast and reach 135 pounds in the Atlantic. Pacific sailfish grow even larger. Sailfish have been clocked at bursts of more than 68 miles per hour, making this fish the fastest swimming fish. Sailfish like warm water and are often found in or near the Gulf Stream.

The deep-bodied blue marlin is found near the surface of the world's open oceans. Females can exceed 1,400 pounds, with males closer to 300 pounds.

HOW ABOUT THAT BILL!

"Swordfish." "Billfish." Those names attempt to describe the single feature of these fishes that is the most prominent. The bill, or rostrum, is really the upper jaw, only greatly extended. Studies involving billfish larvae have shown that the adult's rostrum forms as an extension of the fish's beak-like upper jaw. Some scombrids also have such a beak-like jaw. However, it never reaches the sword-like appearance of billfishes, where the bill exceeds the length of the rest of the head.

The swordfish grows the longest rostrum, and it is flattened in cross section. Billfishes grow a shorter rostrum that is round in cross section. In blue marlin, the rostrum lengthens with age; in sailfish, it shortens.

Bottom: **a sailfish with its dorsal fin raised.**

RH/Seapics.com

Top: a striped marlin.

Right: a blue marlin.

Bottom: a shortbilled spearfish.

All marlins and spearfishes are fast-swimming species of the high seas. They are extremely popular game fishes, but unfortunately they have suffered declines in abundance in many regions because a great many are caught by commercial longline fishermen fishing primarily for tuna.

MU/Seapics.com

MU/Seapics.com

Flatfishes

(Order Pleuronectiformes)

The flatfishes look strange. Biologists say the bodies are highly compressed. That just means they are flat, hence their name. This order of fishes is distributed worldwide, most often on continental slopes, but sometimes in even deeper water. Several members of this order are found in brackish waters, and a few in freshwater habitats. Flatfishes support an important commercial fishery in several countries, including the US.

In most species, the side with the eyes is pigmented, while the blind side (bottom, sort of?) has little, if any pigment. Many flatfishes have spots on their pigmented side, and unlike leopards, the flatfishes can change their spots, so to speak. They can alter their pigmentation remarkably to mimic their surroundings, much like a chameleon. Often flatfishes improve their camouflage by fluttering their bodies on the bottom until they are covered by a fine layer of sand, except for their eyes, which are still alert for food or foe. When flatfishes leave the bottom, they still swim on their sides.

WANDERING EYES

When flatfish larvae hatch from eggs, they look much like other fishes, with eyes on each side of the head. At an early point in their development, one eye or the other begins to move, or migrate, to the side. Those species in which the left eye migrates are called dextral flatfishes. Species in which the right eye migrates are called sinistral flatfishes. As the eye migrates, the fish leans on its side more and more and takes on a truly bizarre appearance. Eventually the eye completes its migration across the top of the head and comes to rest near the other eye. By this time, the fish has come to lie flat on its side on the bottom.

The distance the eye travels varies among species. The eye of some American soles travels only about 1/5 inch, while the eye in some of the leftyeye flounders travels almost five inches. In some flounders, a depression forms between the eyes and in front of the developing dorsal fin, and the migrating eye follows this route. In other species, the eye passes through a gap between the dorsal fin and the head.

The eyes don't travel alone. During the flatfish's metamorphosis, the mouth usually shifts to one side, and the gills and internal organs also rearrange themselves to accommodate the fish's developing asymmetrical shape.

Tonguefishes

(Family Cynoglossidae)

The long, tapering tonguefishes were named for their tongue-shaped bodies. Their tiny eyes are located on the left side of the head, and their dorsal and anal fins are continuous with the tail fin, giving the appearance of a single fin almost encircling the body. Sometimes called tongue soles, tonguefishes live on the bottom where they feed on worms and small crustaceans. Most species prefer mud or sand bottoms, but a few live near reefs.

The blackcheek tonguefish is abundant in Florida's inshore waters over mud bottoms and also ventures into brackish water. Despite its name, the offshore tonguefish is usually found inshore, though it replaces the blackcheek tonguefish in deeper water.

RIGHT EYE OR LEFT EYE

Apart from being flat, this order of fish sports another odd feature: its eyes. Both are located on the same side of the fish's body. Some families have the eyes on the left side, while other families' eyes are on the right. "Left" and "right" don't correspond to "top" and "bottom," however. To recognize the difference in the location of the eyes, locate the fish's pelvic fins and lower jaw. Looking at the fish head-on, in its normal eyes-up position, ask: are the eyes on the left side or the right side of the jaw and pelvic fins? Eyes left—left-eyed species. Eyes right—right-eyed species. That method works for normal flounders only. Rarely, an individual of a left-eyed species will have its eyes on the right side, and vice versa. That's Nature.

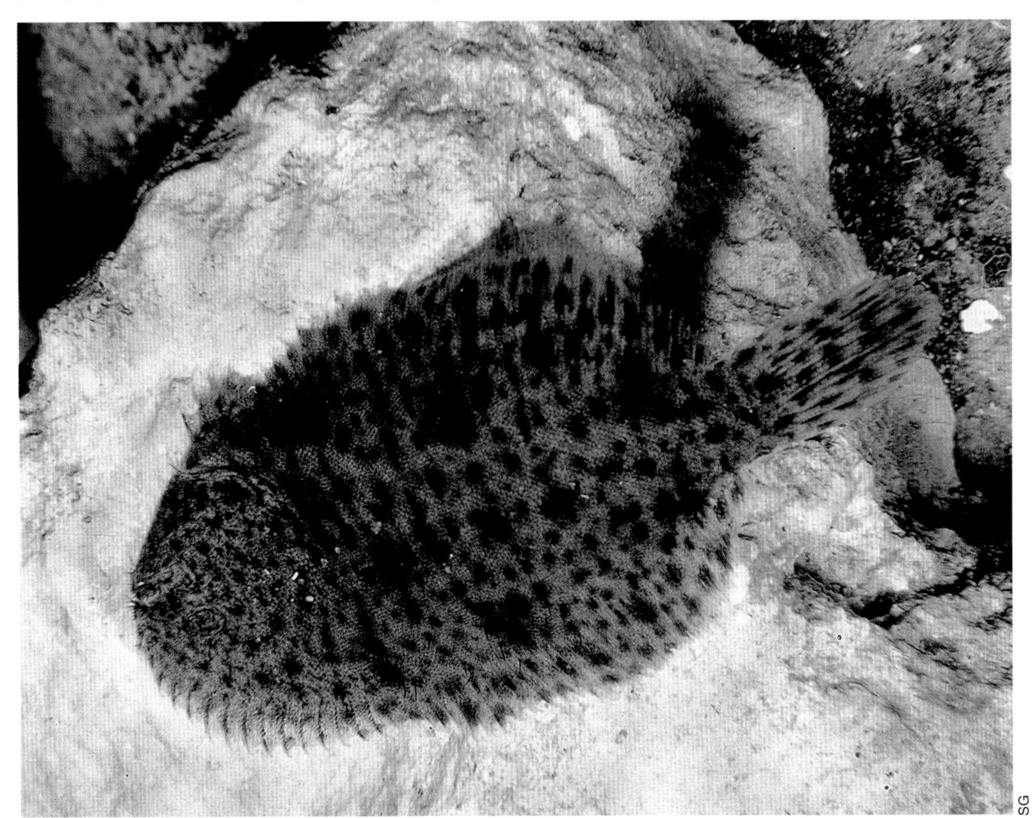

SG

American Soles

(Family Achiridae)

American soles are rather small and have eyes on the right side. They have the ability to adhere to hard surfaces with their blind side.

The hogchoker is found in bays and the shallow Gulf. Its young run upriver into fresh water where they often are caught and sold in the aquarium trade as "freshwater flounder." Hogchokers are said to have been so abundant once they were used to feed hogs, and occasionally one would get caught in a hog's throat and choke it.

***Above:* a hogchoker.**

DP/Seapics.com

Lefteye Flounders

(Families Bothidae and Paralichthyidae)

"Sole" and "flounder" get used interchangeably sometimes, but true soles aren't flounders. These fish belong to different suborders. Flounders are further divided into lefteye families and righteye families. Most righteye flounders live in regions of cold water.

Lefteye flounders lie on their right side with their eyes on their left side. The rare abnormal member of this family gets things all mixed up. This one will wind up with its eyes on its right side and must lie on its left side. Normally the blind side of these fishes is white. On the eyed side, the coloration of most of these flounders is brown. However, they can change color to match their surroundings, from white to dark brown, with all manner of patterns. Flounders eat crustaceans and small fishes.

One of the most common flounders around coral reefs off southeastern Florida is the beautiful peacock flounder. Other Florida flounders include the common Gulf flounder, which migrates from the bays and grass flats into the Gulf at the onset of cold weather, and the spiny flounder, Florida's smallest lefteye flounder at a whopping three inches.

DP/Seapics.com

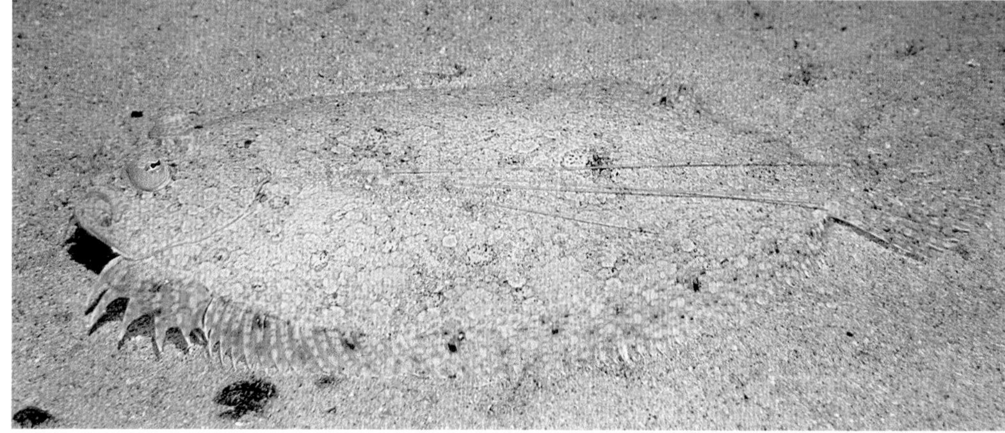

Top: **a peacock flounder.**

Center: **another peacock flounder.**

Bottom: **a peacock flounder camouflages itself by matching the color of the sand.**

DP/Seapics.com

Triggerfishes And Their Allies

INTRODUCTION TO THE ORDER TETRAODONTIFORMES

A diverse group of very specialized fishes makes up this order. They vary in size, shape, and lifestyle, too. They range in size from one inch to ten feet. Despite their diversity, the 350 or so species of this order share some important features. They all have small mouths in comparison to their bodies, with either a few teeth that are often enlarged, or a beak-like tooth plate. A relatively small gill opening is restricted to the side of the head. Usually the scales are modified into a protective covering of some kind. The pelvic fins are either greatly reduced or absent.

Triggerfishes

(Family Balistidae)

Body armor and long dorsal spines characterize triggerfishes. Their common name comes from their "trigger," a ball-and-socket structure associated with the fish's dorsal fin. It enables the second dorsal spine to lock the longer first dorsal spine in an erect position. Most triggerfish like to stay close to reefs or other structures. There, when a triggerfish is threatened by a predator or hooked by an angler, it can dart into a hole, erect its dorsal spines, and depress its pelvic bone. This manuever wedges the triggerfish into the reef. Thick, plate-like scales cover the fish's head and body, rounding out this family's arsenal of armor.

Some triggerfishes display bright colors and intricate patterns. Triggerfishes have small mouths with massive, incisor-like teeth they use to crush the mollusks and crustaceans they feed on. Triggerfishes lay their eggs in a sandy depression and the male guards them. Males of some of the larger species, while guarding their nests, have attacked and bitten divers.

Of the 40 species of triggerfishes worldwide, six are found in Florida's waters. The queen triggerfish is found occasionally on offshore reefs to depths over 300 feet. This species is especially fond of sea urchins. The more common gray triggerfish is found around reefs and pilings.

DDM/Seapics.com

DP/Seapics.com

***Top:* a queen triggerfish.**

***Center:* a sargasssum triggerfish.**

***Above:* a black durgon. Note the distinctive white line at the base of the dorsal and anal fins.**

DP/Seapics.com

Filefishes

(Family Monacanthidae)

The filefishes are closely related to the triggerfishes but have more compressed bodies and much smaller scales. The scales are hardly discernible to the naked eye but give a sandpaper feel to the fish's skin, hence the name. The filefishes are more diversified than triggerfishes and lack the triggerfishes' locking method for the first dorsal spine. The smallest filefish (not a Floridian) matures at less than one inch, while Florida's largest, the scrawled filefish, may exceed three feet. Many filefishes inhabit the same reefs and other structure as triggerfishes, but several species prefer sandy or muddy coastal flats. Filefishes' incisor-like teeth are somewhat delicate and allow for specialized feeding on small invertebrates. Most filefishes' coloration and markings help them blend in with their surroundings.

Filefishes display an especially noticeable feature related to their ventral surface (bottom side). The pelvic bone (there is no fin) supports a flap of skin between itself and the fish's anus. Sometimes called a dewlap, this flap in some species is highly pigmented and may be used in courtship displays, with the movable pelvic bone able to expand or contract the flap.

About 95 species of filefishes live in the tropical and temperate waters of the world. As many as ten species live around Florida and the Caribbean. The rather large whitespotted filefish is a spectacular reef species with two color phases. One phase displays white spots over its head and body. The other phase lacks the white spots, allowing the yellow or orange background colors to show. The planehead filefish is one of Florida's most common inshore filefishes, and the young often enter bays.

MK/Seapics.com

DP/Seapics.com

Top: **a courting pair of whitespotted filefish with one fish in spotted color phase and the other in the saddle phase.**

Center: **a planehead filefish.**

Above: **pygmy filefish.**

Top: whitespotted filefish gather around floating debris in the Atlantic.

Left: a slender filefish.

Below: a fringed filefish.

Bottom: a scrawled filefish.

DDM/Seapics.com

DP/Seapics.com

MK/Seapics.com

DP/Seapics.com

Boxfishes

(Family Ostraciidae)

The remarkable and peculiarly shaped boxfishes, or trunkfishes, wear a suit of armor that helps protect the adults from predators. The young of many species, however, live in the open ocean where they are eaten by many pelagic predators. The bony box that gives this family its common name is formed of modified scales that enclose the body in a rigid "shell", or cuirass. Only the eyes, mouth, fins, and tail are exposed. Because of the rigid covering, boxfishes can swim only by using their extended fins. Boxfishes look roughly triangular in cross section and lack pelvic fins. Some species secrete a poisonous substance from their skin which may help ward off predators.

Boxfishes have been divided into two groups, cowfishes and trunkfishes. Cowfishes have a sharp spine over each eye; trunkfishes lack these spines. They feed primarily on small, clinging creatures and algae and tend to be territorial.

DP/Seapics.com

DP/Seapics.com

Four or five species are found in Florida. Their shells are sometimes sold as souvenirs. The scrawled cowfish has prominent spines over each eye reminiscent of cow horns. This is the most common cowfish of the continental shelf and saltier bays, including the sea grass beds. Common on offshore reefs, the smooth trunkfish bumps along the bottom feeding on benthic invertebrates.

***Top:* a smooth trunkfish, golden phase.**

***Left:* a smooth trunkfish.**

Bottom, left: a honeycomb cowfish.

Bottom, right: a scrawled cowfish. Note the spines over its eyes which are not seen in the trunkfish.

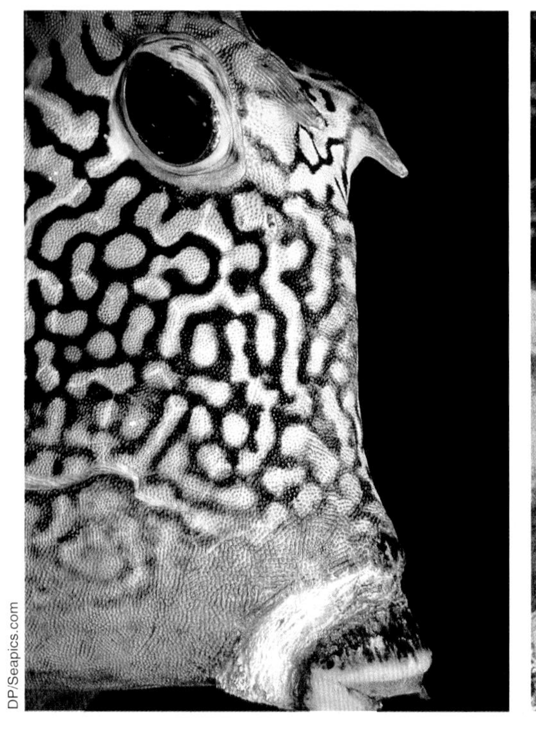

DP/Seapics.com

MK/Seapics.com

MPO/Seapics.com

DELICIOUSLY DEADLY

The flesh of puffers is prized as a delicacy in some countries, notably Japan. Yet many puffers, including some Florida species, contain a highly potent poison concentrated in the liver, ovaries, and other organs, and also found in the skin and blood in varying amounts. The poison, tetrodotoxin, is much stronger than cyanide and attacks the nervous system. Specially licensed restaurants in Japan serve fugu reubripes *(a Japanese puffer) to connoisseurs who like to live on the edge. Unfortunately, not all of those diners continue to live following their meal. Some Asian puffers contain the poison in their flesh and closely resemble supposedly safer species.*

Captain James Cook was offered just a taste of the liver and ovaries of a puffer in New Caledonia during his second exploration of the Pacific Ocean in 1774. He almost died. In recent years, scientists have discovered puffers can secrete this powerful poison into the water when they are alarmed to foil the advance of a predator.

Puffers

(Family Tetraodontidae)

Their family name says it all: *tetra* means "four," and *odont* means "tooth." The teeth of these fish are fused into four plates, two each in the upper and lower jaws, yielding a beak-like mouth well-suited to crushing the shells of invertebrates. Puffers inhabit shallow tropical and temperate waters worldwide, including reefs, estuaries, rivers, and lakes. As their common name implies, puffers can greatly inflate their bodies with air or water until they are nearly round. To accomplish this feat, they pump water or air into a balloon-like sac in the stomach. Puffers lack ribs, so as the sac expands, so does the puffer. Most puffers are covered with small spines or prickles, which protrude from the body when the puffer puffs up. The inflation and the spines make puffers hard to swallow. Most puffers lay their eggs in nests of sorts, some being no more than tufts of algae. Some species are group spawners that may form huge spawning congregations. Spawning seems to be tied to the moon cycle, often occuring several days after a new or full moon.

DP/Seapics.com

Around 120 puffers live around the world. No freshwater puffers occur in Florida, though a South American genus does enter fresh water. The small southern puffer is the common puffer of the northeastern Gulf and occurs along the East Coast of Florida, as well. Breeding males develop small red spots over much of their bodies. The bandtail puffer is a common puffer of shallow reefs around the state and also can be found in sea-grass beds.

***Top:* a sharpnose puffer.**

***Center:* a brandtail puffer.**

THE LATERAL LINE AND OTHER FISH SENSES

Basically, a fish's life boils down to this: finding food and mates while avoiding predators. A fish possesses a complex sensory system that helps it accomplish all those tasks. Some of the details of these sensory systems vary among species, but most share certain general components.

The lateral line is a common feature of most bony fish (sharks and rays do not have a lateral line). A line of scales with pores in them runs down each side of the fish, usually from behind the gills to near the base of the tail. In most fish, these pressure-sensitive pores are connected by fluid-filled tubes, or canals, that extend onto the fish's head. A transparent lump of jelly, or cupula, rests on sensory cells in these tubes, forming a sensory organ called a neuromast. Such sensory cells, or hair cells, are found in the ears of all vertebrates. Neuromasts in fishes are strategically placed in the tube between the openings to the surface of the lateral line. The cupulae project into the tube.

Humans form images of their surroundings from sounds that they hear. It's quite possible that fish form similar images of aquatic surroundings. The lateral line is so sensitive even to weak currents in the dense medium of water that fish can detect even slight disturbances caused by a moving object. They "feel" these disturbances. Thus, the lateral line aids fishes in locating prey, avoiding danger, and perhaps even navigating, particularly in turbid water where sight is limited, or in the dark.

The lateral line also helps people indentify fish. The position, number, and shape of scales in the lateral line provide taxonomic clues.

Most fishes also can hear to a degree, and some hear quite well. Sound waves cause pressure changes in the water that can be sensed by the fish. Most species have only a limited perception of sound. However, species possessing a connection between the ear and swim bladder hear very well. Carps and minnows (Family Cyprinidae) have such a connection of small bones, called the Weberian apparatus, which joins the swim bladder to the ear. The swim bladder is filled with gas. Since a gas bubble in water amplifies sound, the swim bladder improves a fish's hearing. Carps and minnows hear exceptionally well.

DP/Seapics.com

Porcupinefishes
(Family Diodontidae)

Like the puffers, porcupinefishes can inflate their bodies until they are nearly round, but porcupinefishes have larger spines, as well as teeth fused into a single beak in each jaw. Members of this family inhabit the world's shallow tropical and temperate coastal waters, with a few species in the open ocean. The young of the pelagic species sometimes congregate by the thousands. These and the pelagic young of most species of porcupinefishes become food for larger pelagic fishes, such as tunas.

This family is divided into two groups based on the types of spines. Porcupinefishes have long, sharp spines that are erected when the fish inflates. Burrfishes have shorter spines fixed in place. When adult porcupinefishes inflate, they present a prickly sphere too large for most predators to tackle.

Of the 19 species of porcupinefishes known, six are found along Florida's coast. They eat primarily hard-shelled crustaceans and mollusks they crush with their beaks. These fishes are sometimes dried and sold as souvenirs. The balloonfish is fairly common along Gulf and southern Atlantic coasts and grows to almost 20 inches. It ranges from mangrove shorelines to shallow reefs. The hardy striped burrfish is especially common in saltier bays and shallow Gulf.

DP/Seapics.com

***Top:* a bridled burrfish (note the fixed spines)**
***Above:* a porcupinefish.**

DP/Seapics.com

DP/Seapics.com

MK/Seapics.com

Top: a balloonfish. Note how the spines deploy only when the fish inflates itself, in contrast to the fixed spines of the burrfish.

Center: a balloonfish without inflation.

Bottom: a striped burrfish.

RH/Seapics.com

Molas
(Ocean Sunfish)
(Family Molidae)

The giant mola, or ocean sunfish, is the largest bony fish in the world, sometimes exceeding ten feet both in length and two tons in weight. The whale shark is bigger, but has a skeleton of cartilage, not bone. Mola means "millstone" in Latin, and that describes the general shape of this gentle giant. Some people have likened the shape to a lima bean.

The mola often sticks its fins out of the water as the fish lolls about at the surface, and their fins have been mistaken for the dorsal fin of a shark. But, these fish are hardly a threat to humans. They are fond of jellyfish and also eat squid, crustaceans and small fish. Great white sharks and killer whales prey on molas.

Molas can swim by waving their dorsal and anal fins and using their "tail" as a rudder. They also steer by jetting water from their mouths or gills. Surprisingly, these docile fish have been reported to jump ten feet into the air.

It seems unlikely that huge molas would be included in the same order with puffers and porcupinefishes. However, molas share enough characteristics with those families to link them. For example, molas have a single beak-like tooth plate in each jaw, like porcupinefishes. Ocean sunfish are not related to the freshwater sunfishes.

The species in this strange family have such abbreviated bodies they look chopped off. Sometimes called headfishes for that reason, molas lack a true tail fin. Instead, the rear dorsal and anal fin rays form a fin-like structure at the rear of the body.

Molas occupy most of the world's tropical and temperate seas and are not rare far offshore, just rarely seen. They can be encountered anywhere off Florida's coasts. Sometimes one comes visiting near to shore. Occasional specimens wash up dead on beaches, and live molas are sometimes sighted lying quietly on their sides on the ocean's surface, or slowly feeding on drifts of jellyfishes. Amazingly, one female may produce 300 million tiny eggs.

Three species are known. Two of these reach giagantic proportions. One specimen weighed 4,400 pounds. Also found off both coasts is the much smaller slender mola, which is only about 32 inches in length.

VU - RH

JW/Seapics.com

Top: a mola with diver showing the huge size of this fish.

Above: molas like to drift along the surface. When they raise a fin above the water, they are sometimes mistaken for a shark when viewd from a distance.

Bottom: a view of a mola showing the "sawed-off" appearance of the mola "tail fin."

INDEX

INDEX *(cont'd)*

FLORIDA AQUARIUMs

JP

The Sunshine State is fortunate to have a number of interesting aquariums where many fish and other sea life can be observed. The list below varies from enormous, popular tourist attractions, like Sea World, to small and out of the way places of interest, like Gulf Specimen Company. All will be rewarding visits. Many of these organizations have educational programs for the young and others engaged in rescue, particularly of porpoise, turtles, and whales.

Clearwater Aquarium (727-441-1790)
249 Windwood Passage, Clearwater FL 33767.

Florida Aquarium (813-273-4000)
701 Channelside Drive, Tampa FL 33602
www.flaquarium.org

Gulf Specimen Company (850-984-5297)
222 Clark Drive, Panacea FL 32346

Key West Aquarium (305-296-2051)
1 Whitehead Street, Key West FL 33040
www.KeyWestAquarium.com

Marineland (904-460-1275)
9600 Ocean Shore Boulevard, Marineland FL 32080

Mote Marine Laboratory (941-388-4441)
1600 Ken Thompson Parkway, Sarasota FL 34236
www.mote.org

Sea World (407-351-3600)
Prominently Located at I-4 and SR-528 in Orlando
www/seaworld.com

Theater of the Sea (305-664-2431)
84721 Overseas Highway, Islamorada FL 33036
www.theaterofthesea.com